EGGS, FISH AND BANANA LEAVES

EGGS, FISH AND BANANA LEAVES

Ruth Shakeshaft
with Lindy Greaves

MILTON KEYNES • COLORADO SPRINGS • HYDERABAD

14 13 12 11 10 09 08 8 7 6 5 4 3 2 1

First published 2008 by Authentic Media
9 Holdom Avenue, Bletchley, Milton Keynes, MK1 1QR, UK
1820 Jet Stream Drive, Colorado Springs, CO 80921, USA
Medchal Road, Jeedimetla Village, Secunderabad 500 055, A.P., India
www.authenticmedia.co.uk

Authentic Media is a division of IBS-STL U.K., limited by guarantee, with its Registered Office at Kingstown Broadway, Carlisle, Cumbria CA3 0HA. Registered in England & Wales No. 1216232. Registered charity 270162

British Library Cataloguing in Publication Data
A catalogue record for this book is available from the British Library

ISBN-13: 978-1-85078-798-3

Cover Design by fourninezero design.
Print Management by Adare
Printed in Great Britain by J.H. Haynes & Co., Sparkford

Contents

Acknowledgements

During the writing and preparation of this book for publication, I have received help and encouragement from many friends who have cajoled and bullied me into finishing the task. In particular, I am grateful to Ann Holden who helped with the technical bits, liaising with The Leprosy Mission and Authentic Media and designing the first draft of the book cover. My friend of many years, Steph Golden, set me off on the writing road by buying me my computer. Judith Burgess came to my aid whenever my computer threw a fit of temper, which was often!

I would also like to thank Judith Merrell at TLM for her initial interest in the book and for the work that she, Kath Williams at Authentic Media, and Sheila Jacobs (the editor) have put in to make it all happen.

I would like to pay special tribute to the late Sr Alcantara FMSA, who was in charge at Buluba during my time there. But for her support, interest and wholehearted encouragement, the Leprosy Control System, as developed in Busoga district, would not have been possible.

Ruth Shakeshaft, 2008

Acknowledgements

Foreword

Ruth's book vividly portrays the joy and hardship of missionary work in Uganda in the twentieth century. We enter the world of people suffering from leprosy: people who were often shunned by their families and by the societies in which they lived. Ruth herself made a huge contribution to the foundation of successful medical treatment and care for these people, gaining their respect and friendship. In turn, she came to love this beautiful country and its people who, in spite of their suffering, were full of joy and the celebration of life.

Eggs, Fish and Banana Leaves is to be welcomed, not only for its importance in the history of medical missionary work, but because it is a very human story.

Dr Wanda Blenska
Leprologist to Busoga district, Buluba Leprosy Centre and Nyenga Leprosy Centre in Buganda.
Now retired and living in her native Poland

1.

Buried Alive!

I first met Waiswa when I helped to lift him from his grave. His eyes were sunken deep into their sockets by dehydration, his lips were cracked and dry and he muttered softly in the delirium of fever. As I gently brushed the earth from his stricken face, his eyes focused briefly on mine.

'Thank you,' he whispered.

This was during an outbreak of plague in Uganda; the mortality rate was high and people dying from the disease were very quickly buried in shallow graves, often within three hours of death. Fortunately for Waiswa, it was not the custom to nail the deceased into wooden coffins: bodies were simply wrapped in barkcloth. Waiswa had obviously been desperately ill but not yet dead when he had been buried in haste. Just below the earth's surface, warmed by the African sun penetrating the soil, Waiswa stirred. He managed to work an arm free of the barkcloth bindings and dislodge the overlying earth. A passer-by saw a weakly waving hand emerge from the ground and, believing it to be a sinister manifestation, ran screaming to the mission station (a perfectly understandable reaction in the circumstances!).

Three of us hurried from the mission station to the site of the waving hand and managed to exhume the rest of the body, to the accompaniment of many cries and exclamations from the onlookers who wisely kept their distance. We carried the desperately emaciated Waiswa straight to the mission hospital, where for several days he remained seriously ill. Gradually, with the benefit of good nursing care, he made a full recovery.

When the time came for Waiswa to leave hospital, I had the privilege of driving him home. It was an unforgettable day. As we neared his village, more and more people came out to line the road, until hundreds were gathered to welcome home their Lazarus. Everywhere, people were singing, clapping and dancing with joy. At last we reached Waiswa's home, to find the compound decorated with flowers and palms. His wife and children were waiting for him, dressed in their very best native clothes. The men of the village wore beautifully embroidered *kanzus*, long white robes, usually made of linen. The ladies wore their traditional *gayazas*, long wrap-over gowns buttoned at the neck with short sleeves and a wide, brightly coloured sash with a long fringe.

As Waiswa stepped out of the car, everyone, including his wife, knelt down and bowed to him, in a deeply touching greeting. He and his wife entered their little house, leaving everybody else outside to talk and celebrate together. Later the drums began to beat and a feast was laid out for all to enjoy.

After the feasting, there was dancing. Both dancers and onlookers were fortified by the local home brew. I was courteously offered a cup of tea for which I was grateful. Sadly, I soon had to wish Waiswa and his family farewell, as it was important that I returned to the mission before sunset, some thirty miles away, over very rough terrain.

Several months later Waiswa visited the mission, bringing with him the gift of a goat and some eggs for the patients to eat and enjoy. He had made such a full recovery it was hard to believe we had dug him out of a grave! Everyone was delighted to see how well and happy he looked. At the same time he offered to help with the work of the mission in any way possible. The missioner-in-charge discussed the matter with the staff and it was decided that Waiswa should be trained as a hospital orderly.

Over the ensuing years, Waiswa became much more than an orderly: he took out teeth and gave general anaesthetics, which in the 1950s consisted of a mixture of chloroform and ether dropped onto a mask placed over the face of the patient. He became most proficient at this, administering hundreds of anaesthetics over the years, during which time we had no fatalities related to the anaesthetic itself.

Waiswa possessed that very special gift of always having time for people; time to listen and give advice, especially to the relatives of patients who were so worried. Both patients and their families often had no idea of what a hospital was about and were frequently very frightened by what they saw happening. Waiswa became the confidante of many a young missionary, including myself, who found the language and the customs difficult. He was especially helpful when these 'African novices' were homesick and lonely. I remember him as a gentle, courteous person, who was greatly missed when he finally died in the early 1970s.

2.

The Leaving of Liverpool

But how did I, a young woman from a village in the north-west of England, come to meet Waiswa, deep in the African bush?

Was my father responsible? He had always been so keen for me to read and broaden my knowledge, buying books for me at Christmas and for my birthday. He considered that I should be every bit as well educated as my older brother and not miss opportunities through the chance of being a daughter.

Perhaps it was Miss Kelly's fault? As my Sunday school teacher at the village church, it was she who had first implanted the seeds of Africa, encouraging her pupils to make weekly donations of one (pre-decimalisation) penny from their meagre pocket money to support the work of missionaries in Africa. The letters and occasional sepia photograph that resulted from our largesse fascinated me and I made a childish resolve that one day I would see these places for myself.

Or was it my own personal and private sadness that drew me, as a young woman, to the religious life and missionary work, forsaking all that convention expected of me?

Certainly, I didn't come from a family of explorers. I was the second child and only daughter of Henry (known as Harry), a farmer, and Ellen Shakeshaft. I was born on 19 October 1921, in the village of Pensby, Wirral, in what was then Cheshire and is now Merseyside. My brother, Will, was older than me by eight years. My upbringing was no different from that of countless others in the England of the first half of the twentieth century. My parents worked hard and did their best to ensure that Will and I never went hungry, and received the best available education.

At that time, before the girth of the Merseyside commuter belt widened, Pensby was a small village in which everyone knew everyone else. The presiding authorities were the local policeman and the vicar. The policeman was a man with high standards and not above giving misbehaving boys a clout when he thought they deserved such treatment.

We were brought up to believe in God so the local church, Christ Church in Barnston, figured largely in our weekly routine. Dad was a sidesman, welcoming visitors, showing them to their seats and then taking their money during the collection hymn. My brother and I were regular Sunday school attendees and I was also a member of the choir. I joined the 1st Barnston Brownie pack and, in time, flew over the toadstool (the Brownie initiation ceremony into the Guides!) into the Girl Guides and then Rangers. At home, too, we were taught to thank Jesus for the new day as we awoke each morning. In the evening, we said our prayers together, as a family. One night, when I should have been in bed, I passed my parents' open bedroom door and saw them kneeling, side by side, at the foot of their bed, saying their own evening prayers.

Will and I each went to school in nearby Heswall. As I was so much younger, Will would take me to my school first, perching me on the crossbar of his bike, and then collect me at the end of the day. There was a skill involved in balancing on the front of the bike whilst trying not to drop my books or the meat and potato pies Mother had made for our lunch.

In common with many men of his generation in the north of England, Dad was a pigeon fancier and we had a pigeon loft in the back garden. Every Saturday afternoon, there was a race; we sat in the garden, willing the returning pigeons to go into the pigeon loft. Until the pigeon actually went into the loft, it wasn't considered to have crossed the finishing line of the race, so imagine our frustration when a bird wandered aimlessly about on the loft roof, instead of going in! Once a bird had deigned to re-enter the loft, we worked quickly to remove its racing ring and to record its arrival time. At five o'clock in the afternoon, everybody gathered at the village centre, with the flight times for each of their birds to discover whose pigeon had won.

By 1937, I was working as a junior nurse at Cleaver Sanatorium in Heswall while waiting to take up my place on a general nursing course at St Catherine's Hospital in Birkenhead. Although it was near my parents' house, I had to sleep at the hospital. I spent my days off with my parents but was only allowed to stay overnight with them if I obtained a pass. The junior nurses on our ward nicknamed the ward sister 'Sister Tut', as she would run her finger along a windowsill we should have dusted, shake her head and tut.

One night in particular will always stay with me: I was asleep in the nurses' home and had a dream that was more like a vision. I was walking along a very wide road, with my mother and father on either side of me. Gradually I moved ahead of them, and found myself walking towards something that I realised was the feet of Jesus on the cross. I didn't see the whole of Jesus' body or the cross, only his feet. And I found myself leaving my parents far behind, whilst I struggled to reach his feet. Over the next few days, while I was going about my work on the ward, parts of this dream or vision recurred to me repeatedly and vividly. Although I didn't attach any particular significance to this at the time, I wonder now if it was the first premonition that I would be a missionary.

The Second World War, which broke out in 1939, pervaded the whole of my general nursing training at St Catherine's. A hospital must have been one of the only places where no one reacted when the air raid siren went off. Since Birkenhead is directly opposite the major seaport of Liverpool, across the River Mersey, there were bombing raids on the docks and the city most nights. Soon after the howls of the warning sirens had faded away, the casualties would arrive: those close to death, with terribly mutilated bodies, others pale with shock and blood loss and missing limbs, and still others burned black by the bomb blast or the fires which raged afterwards.

Worst of all were the young children who had been caught in a blast. Those of us old enough to understand had been taught that if a bomb exploded nearby, we should throw ourselves onto the ground and cover our faces to avoid collapsed lungs. Little children, too young for these survival lessons, were brought to us by the ambulances. They looked as if they were sleeping, often without a scratch on their tiny bodies, but their breath had been blown out of them and they were quite dead.

Although we were kept busy, I soon made some good friends. Living at the hospital, away from our families, and in the shadow of war, threw us together, and I became close to two other trainee nurses. All the trainees were called by their surnames: so the three of us were

Shakeshaft, Ollerhead and Wilkinson. We were soon known as Shakie, Ollie and Wilkie.

One day, we all managed to get the same night off so we could to go to Birkenhead to the theatre. During the day, I committed some minor crime in the nursing rule-book and was hauled into the matron's office. I confessed, hoping she would be lenient. However, Matron told me that she was cancelling my night off and, in addition, I would have to work a shift. I was disappointed but nevertheless encouraged Ollie and Wilkie to go to the theatre without me, as no one knew when next we would all have the same night off. While my friends dressed up to go out, I prepared for my shift. That night there was a direct hit on the theatre in Birkenhead and Ollie and Wilkie were both killed.

During the second year of my training I had some contact with the Carmelite nuns in Birkenhead. The war was forcing me to evaluate the direction I wanted my life to take; I was receiving a valuable training and I wanted to work and put the training to good use. I discussed this with the nuns and found that they were sympathetic. Some of them felt that, though I hadn't yet realised it myself, I had a missionary vocation. One of the Carmelite Sisters had a close friend who had joined the Franciscan Missionary Sisters for Africa. She suggested I make an application to Holme Hall, the convent of this Order in Yorkshire. I would be a novice for six months, after which I could leave if I didn't feel that it was right for me. I completed my general training in Birkenhead and decided to go to Yorkshire.

Despite the strict rules of the Order, the novitiate period was very happy. During one of our recreation times, when I was fairly new to Holme Hall, I was sitting at the piano surrounded by some of the other novices. Earlier that week I had bought the sixpenny sheet music of 'It's a Sin to Tell a Lie' and was playing and singing it at the top of my voice when the door opened and the novice mistress strode in. With a horror-struck face she removed the music from the piano. I never saw it again! Fortunately my misdemeanour was forgiven and, after the initial six months, I continued at Holme Hall for a further two years. I had arrived as Ruth Shakeshaft, but left as Sister Aelred.

The Franciscan Missionary Sisters for Africa had adapted its rules to make these more appropriate for missionaries. We had to say our prayers, of course, but not at set times of day, so if I was required to help with an emergency during morning prayer time, I could postpone my prayers until later. The sisters who were involved in missionary training were all former missionaries themselves and knew what skills might best equip us. They thought that, since I'd qualified as a nurse, it would be beneficial for me to study midwifery. So after my years at Holme Hall, I went to the district hospital in Cork, Ireland, to train as a midwife. The culmination of all this training was that the Franciscan Missionary Sisters for Africa decided I was fit to become a missionary and that I would soon leave for Uganda. I knew that, according to the rules of our Order at that time, once I had arrived in Africa, I would never be allowed to return to England.

So, did I feel a thrill of adventure as I stood on the deck of the *SS Orbita*, with the tugs manoeuvring the ship slowly away from the Liverpool dockside? Did I feel impatient to be gone as I watched the faces of my dear parents fade into the amorphous mass of the watching crowd? Was I looking forward to landfall in Africa, knowing that I might never come home? All I remember was an engulfing misery, and the inklings of a plan to persuade the captain to put me ashore at the earliest opportunity, and most definitely before we had left British waters.

I had been delighted to discover that we were to sail from Liverpool, as I hoped there would be an opportunity to see my parents before leaving the country. I had it all planned. We were even going to stay at the convent in Birkenhead, after our journey from Yorkshire, until it was time to go to the docks. The convent was only a short walk from my parents' house and there were several hours to spare before we had to embark. Sister Bede was the most senior of our party travelling to Uganda and was therefore in charge, so once we'd arrived at the convent, I asked her whether I could go to see my parents. She denied my request and I didn't question her. I expect she thought it wasn't appropriate as I was the only Sister whose parents lived nearby (the other Sisters were all Irish).

Later that afternoon, the Wednesday of Holy Week (also known as Spy Wednesday) in 1947, we took the bus and the ferry across the Mersey to Liverpool. Arriving at the docks, I was told that my parents were there, waiting to see me, but again I was not allowed to speak to them. I knew that only a few days before, my parents had been informed that my brother Will, who they'd been notified as being missing in action in 1944, was still alive but seriously injured. He had been repatriated to a hospital in the south of England. I would have given anything to be able to have a few last words with them.

As the troopship pulled away across Liverpool Bay, bound for Mombasa on the Kenyan coast, I stayed alone on the gently throbbing deck long after my companions had gone to find their quarters; I stayed until I started to shiver. Eventually I went below to join the other Sisters in locating our sleeping quarters and sorting out our belongings. I suppose I must have slept, that first night, because I remember the grim reality of waking up the following morning. Overnight, the even tremor of the ship slipping through calm waters had changed to an erratic plunging and the only way I could minimise the waves of nausea was by keeping my eyes tightly closed. I forced myself to stand, thinking that I might feel better if I went outside. The waves were breaking high over the side of the ship, repeatedly flooding the deck. Though the fresh air relieved my nausea, I thought I might instead be in danger of death by drowning, rather than seasickness, and quickly retreated below.

There were berths for twenty people in our cabin. The six of us from the Franciscan Sisters shared it with Sisters from the Church Missionary Society. As I attempted to sleep, amidst sounds of retching on all sides, I realised that I was not the only one suffering. I felt a cool hand on my head; Sister Bede had brought me a bucket. She'd also brought one for Sister de Sales.

For three impossibly long days I was seasick, wondering why on earth I had chosen to be on this ship, and even how long it might take for me to die. Towards the end of this period, I was half asleep and trying to remain that way, when alarm bells shattered the relative peace. As I opened my eyes to the now familiar view of the wooden slats of the bunk above me, I realised with dismay that the bells meant an evacuation drill. The bunk above creaked as Sister Bede lowered herself to the floor.

'Are you coming, Sister Aelred?' she asked me. 'I think we're supposed to go up to the deck.'

'I know.'

'Shall I wait for you, Sister?'

'No thanks. I think I'll stay here.'

She looked at me for a few seconds before joining the throng making for the door of the cabin and the deck. I tried to ignore the alarm by putting my head under the pillow. After a few moments the ringing finally ceased. I cautiously peeped out to find I was alone in the cabin. I rolled onto my side, hoping I hadn't been rude to Sister Bede. I must have fallen asleep, because the next thing I remember was a man's voice with a thick Liverpudlian accent demanding to know why I was still in my cabin.

'What do you think would've happened if the ship'd been hit by a torpedo?'

There were no torpedoes at that time, but still a chance of a rogue mine floating about. I realised that this was the steward's Liverpudlian sense of humour. With a sigh I turned to face him. 'I think,' I began slowly, 'that *whatever* had happened would've been preferable to the way I'm feeling now.'

And, like all those who have suffered the sheer misery that is seasickness, after four days I found my sea legs and began to enjoy the voyage. Not only did it begin to feel more like an adventure than an evil to endure, but being confined on the ship gave me time to reflect on all the experiences and decisions which had led me to this point, and to look ahead to what my future in Africa might hold. My three years of missionary training had prepared me in some way, but I'd spent so much time learning and training that I hadn't given myself much time to think. Even when I'd been training as a nurse, I had read, played tennis or gone swimming. I'd always managed to keep myself busy.

On Easter Sunday, Sister Bede and I rose very early and went up to the top deck. Everyone else was still in their bunks. If anyone had stumbled up to the deck as dawn broke, they would have been treated to our private rendition of the 'Salve Regina'. Sister Bede had a beautiful voice and I could sing in tune. There was no land in sight in any direction. As we sang, we felt the awesome insignificance of our fleeting lives, compared with the vastness of the sea beneath and the sky above. We felt a sense of peace; God's way, perhaps, of preparing us for the following morning.

3.

Destination Africa

'Sister Aelred? Sister Bede? Are you awake?'

I opened my eyes to the slats above.

'Sister Aelred?'

One of the young Sisters from the Church Missionary Society was peering down at me.

'Can I help you?' I asked.

'It's the captain. He's at the door. He's asking for a midwife and I thought you said you were trained.'

'She is, Sister, and so am I.' Sister Bede lowered herself off the top bunk. 'Now, be quick, Sister,' she said to me as she pulled on her boots. I followed suit and within minutes we were standing outside the cabin with the captain. His sun-browned face was pale beneath the tan, his forehead creased with concern.

'Do either of you happen to be a midwife?'

'We both are,' Sister Bede affirmed. 'Now, how can we help?'

'Well,' the captain looked at his feet and took a breath. 'Last night one of the passengers unexpectedly gave birth to a premature baby.'

Sister Bede nodded, but he didn't elaborate.

'And the ship's doctor?'

'Only recently qualified. Hasn't exactly had much experience of delivering babies. We're a troopship, Sister

– we're not prepared for this sort of thing; we don't even have a nurse on board.'

Sister Bede nodded again. 'Can you take us to them, Captain?'

The captain looked relieved as he led us to our patients in the bowels of the ship. The deeper we went the hotter the air became.

'Good preparation for Africa, Sister!' I mused. She didn't reply and we reached the hospital cabin in silence. I'd had experience of premature babies before, but always in a well-equipped hospital. The young doctor had done his best in delivering the baby. Once we arrived, he showered us with cotton wool and disinfectant, happy to watch while we got on with washing the baby. The mother was terrified. She hadn't been due for a couple of months and had been travelling to meet her husband, who was a police officer in the colonial police force in Kenya. She certainly hadn't expected to give birth in transit – had the captain suspected she might go into labour during the journey he probably wouldn't have let her on board.

It was hard to get the mother to feed the baby, as he was so small and her anxiety made it difficult for her to express milk. Sister Bede and I had very little spare time, day or night, as the mother needed constant reassurance and support.

The *SS Orbita* was in the Mediterranean by the time the baby was born so the captain radioed ahead to the European hospital at Port Said, in Egypt, where we were due to stop a few days later. The day before we reached Port Said, we weighed the baby for the last time in the scales we'd borrowed from the ship's cook. We were delighted to see that he'd put on weight and his mother was now finding it easier to feed him. When the ship docked, a nurse from the European hospital met mother and baby. She was to accompany them by train to Mombasa, where the woman's husband would be waiting for them.

At dinner on the evening before we were due to arrive at Port Said, the captain had announced that as we would be staying for some hours, we would be allowed ashore. After so long on the boat, the thought of walking on land was very appealing. The captain had advised us to change into our tropical outfits because the Egyptian heat would be excessive. For me and the other Franciscan Sisters, this meant exchanging our brown and white habits for pure white ones. He'd stressed the importance of wearing our topees as he didn't want us returning to the boat with sunstroke.

'And don't be persuaded to buy anything. Just be firm!' he'd added.

The next morning, we stood on deck, squinting in the bright sunlight, as the boat glided into port. There was a splash, and then another – natives jumping and diving into the water. Soon there were hundreds of them. They swam right up to the boat trying to sell us their goods: baskets of fruit, eggs, monkeys and jewellery, some of which they held above the water while they swam, shouting in their native tongue. Although we spoke none of their language, they made sure we understood by their expressive mimes. Some of them were just asking for money. Sister Bede carried only a small amount of money for our expenses, and the rest of us had none at all – so any purchases were out of the question, however desirable the goods appeared.

The men yelling as they secured the boat; camels bellowing; traders screeching out the prices of their spices – all created a brilliant cacophony of noise. The perfumes of the spices and sandalwood wafted up to deck level, mingling with the less exotic odours of massed humanity and open drains. It seemed that anything one could possibly want could be bought at one or other of the various stalls. It was nothing like even the most rumbustious of English markets. I observed from the deck that no transaction could take place, it seemed, without being accompanied by frenzied bartering. As we shuffled down the ramp and tried to pick our way through the throng, the heat and smell of the camels became oppressive. Within minutes we were surrounded by hordes of noisy Arabs. They all shouted at once, badgering us to buy their goods or offering to take us on sightseeing tours of the port. Each insisted his price was the best. One in particular was so persistent that he managed to attach himself to our party. We were able to understand a little of his broken English and, finally, we accepted his offer as tour guide.

So we set off after him, trailed by some of the more eager traders. First, our guide took us to the mosque. We had to remove our shoes before going inside. I removed mine reluctantly, worried that they might be stolen if I left them outside. But as I tried to enter carrying them in my hands, one of the other Arabs took them from me, telling me I was not allowed to take them indoors.

The interior of the mosque was not as spectacular as our guide had led us to believe, but still interesting.

Next, we were taken to meet the Roman Catholic Bishop of Port Said. The bishop was very old and spoke only in French. He seemed very fragile as he exchanged greetings with Sister Bede. I didn't listen to their whole conversation, as I was distracted by the bishop's bookcase. When I looked up, the bishop was no longer in the room. He returned moments later, his long grey beard fluttering with excitement as he produced his butterfly collection for us. Here were magnificent specimens of all colours and sizes, mounted and labelled, in large boxes with glass fronts. It was evidently his passion but I'm afraid I may have insulted him when I declared how much I disapproved of killing all these beautiful creatures just to stick pins in them for display. They have a short enough life anyway!

After this we were taken to a convent of Spanish nuns. They showed us their ornate chapel; inside, the cheery streaks of blues and golds seemed to make it glow with warmth. It made the interior of the mosque seem drab in comparison. Once we'd finished looking around there, one of the nuns exclaimed that we must see the Mother Superior. She informed us that the Mother Superior had a reputation for great holiness. The Sister led us to a small room and left us to wait. We perched on our seats, thinking of some of the different saints we'd learned about, eyes shining at the idea of meeting someone really holy. We stood as the door of the room opened and a tall, slim and beautiful person glided in. She smiled warmly and told us to sit down. Her graciousness was almost tangible. She poured tea while she asked us questions about our journey so far and our expectations of Africa. Her accent was English. As she spoke and gave us our drinks, I pictured her as an aristocrat – wearing a black choker and dispensing afternoon tea to her friends – a typical English lady.

As the conversation drew to a close, the elegant Mother Superior said to us, 'Now, my dears, I want to give you some advice for your future lives as missionaries.'

She put her hands in the air and her palms together. I realised I was holding my breath.

'My dears, if you don't eat in Africa, Africa will eat you!'

No one said anything. I felt deflated. We had all been expecting some profound and deeply spiritual advice –

and this wasn't it. Later, after I'd spent several months in Uganda, I realised how true her words had been.

At the end of a very hot and dusty tour of Port Said, we returned to the *Orbita* to continue our journey into the Suez Canal.

Finally we arrived in Mombasa, Kenya. We'd been on the boat for over three weeks. I wondered to myself how the mother and baby we'd helped had managed on their train journey from Egypt. They would have arrived in Mombasa several days ahead of us. Sister Bede and I hoped they were progressing well but we had no way of finding out.

After going through Customs and Immigration we were taken to our train compartment. Our final destination was Kampala, Uganda – a two-day train journey from Mombasa. We were pleasantly surprised at how luxurious and clean the compartment was. There were two bunks in each, so our group of six occupied three compartments; I was sharing with Sister Bede.

While we were on the *Orbita*, we had made friends with a group from the Church Missionary Society, also travelling to Kampala. We had just settled in our seats and were waiting for the train to move off when one of the Missionary Society members appeared in our carriage. Smiling, he (a doctor) presented us with a basket of fruit containing bananas, limes and oranges – all of which we had not seen since war began (nearly eight years before).

'I wanted the honour of being the first to present you with one of the glories of Africa!' he said. It was humid on the train and the fruit was refreshing.

The carriage had huge wide windows, so once the train had moved off I settled down and allowed myself to be absorbed in my first sights of Africa. Although the train was steam-powered, it didn't move at any great speed. This meant we were able not only to see the countryside but also the laughing faces of the Africans waving as the train passed by.

At the third station stop the driver swung the water tube out over the platform, to discharge the hot water before taking on more cold water. Immediately, local people appeared, clutching tin containers to collect the waste hot water. A few children's faces appeared at the window, one grinning mischievously. This particular boy took a step back from the carriage and did a little dance right there on the platform until the train moved off. We were treated to similar scenes each time the train stopped to offload hot water.

At some stations, Sisters came to welcome us to Africa. It was encouraging to meet others who were already living the life that we were about to begin. Many of them we knew by name, but had not met before. What we didn't appreciate at the time was that many had travelled for several days from their missions just to get to the station in time to greet us.

When I was ready to get into my bunk at the end of the day, I rolled up the blind on the window just to see what was out there. I gasped at the beauty of the night sky – without light pollution the myriad of stars almost dazzled me. I'd never seen them so clear and bright – it gave me the illusion I could reach out and touch them. There were constellations I recognised, but their orientation was different. It was a strange thought that my parents could be looking up and seeing the same sky – the same stars – all those miles away.

I enjoyed the whole train journey, not just for those precious first sights of Africa, but for the unexpected luxury the train afforded. The staff were overwhelmingly friendly and the meals were more lavish than anything I'd been accustomed to before.

We finally arrived in Kampala on St George's Day, 1947. Some of the Sisters who were stationed in the capital were waiting on the platform to meet us. As we walked out of the station the first thing we saw was a tarmac road. I was suddenly so overwhelmed with disappointment that I burst into tears – I hadn't expected to see such a modern amenity in Africa. I was trying to quiet myself when I overheard one of the Sisters asking Sister Bridget why I was crying. She said she thought I was homesick. But it wasn't that – after years of imagining Africa a certain way, seeing a different reality crushed me. I thought perhaps I shouldn't have come. It's strange that the sight of a road could have had that effect. I confess I was relieved to discover that it was only half a mile long.

We were taken by car to Nsambya where we were to spend the night. On the short journey, I stared dismally out of the window – it was so disappointingly urban – not like the mud-hutted tribal Africa I had dreamed of. Nsambya was the headquarters of the Sisters in Uganda and also the large hospital training school for nurses and midwives. Before I went to bed, I noticed that the bottom three inches of my white habit were red from the dust. I tried to wash it out in the sink but couldn't remove it all. That night it was difficult to sleep, knowing that the next morning we would be given our appointments to our various mission stations. When I did drift off, I dreamed of lions and red dirt tracks and children dancing around open fires.

4.

The Challenges of Nsambya and a Bush Hospital

There was a mood of uneasy anticipation at the breakfast table that morning. The previous night had been the first in more than three weeks that we'd slept in a proper bed on land, rather than a bunk. The lack of motion had taken a little getting used to. Although I was anxious to discover where I was to be posted, the thought of being separated from the other Sisters was daunting. We'd shared so much in the short time we'd known each other.

After breakfast, we were told to take our first dose of malaria medication. Sister Bede produced a bottle and set it on the table. Sister Bridget reached for it first – to get it over with, she said. It was quinine, in liquid form. I watched her pour the white liquid onto a spoon, place it in her mouth and swallow quickly. Her reaction didn't inspire confidence. I knew taking medication for malaria had to become part of my daily routine so when she put down the bottle I took it next. On closer inspection, the liquid had a blue sheen. I was about to smell it but thought better of it and tipped the spoon into my mouth. I blinked at the bitterness of the viscous liquid and swallowed it as quickly as I could. Once we had all completed the little ritual, we sat expectantly awaiting the announcement of our appointments.

The Sister-in-charge at Nsambya warned us that we must always use the mosquito nets that were attached to each bedstead: 'Now Sisters, wherever in the country you are posted, you must always sleep under your net.' She looked round at each of us. 'And remember, if ever you are called out at night, make sure you tuck the edges of the net tightly under the mattress before you leave – otherwise you may find you have an unwelcome visitor on your return!'

'Where will I actually be sleeping, though?' I said to myself, picturing a wall made of mud with the open sky above me. We all nodded in quiet acquiescence, and finally the waiting was over.

Sister Bede and Sister de Sales were appointed to mission stations in the north of the country, Sister Bridget was to go to the north-east and the other two to different missions north-west of Kampala. I was to stay at Nsambya, taking responsibility for the operating theatre and children's ward. I tried to smile as I said goodbye and God bless to the other Sisters, but inside I felt something not dissimilar to the seasickness that I had experienced on the *Orbita*. I expect I had been chosen to stay at Nsambya because I was a qualified nurse and midwife.

'Sister Aelred, you have an hour before I show you round Nsambya.' Mother Cecilia, the Sister-in-charge, smiled. 'You'll be staying in the cubicle you slept in last night.'

I spent the hour in prayer, trying to subdue all my misguided ideas that being a missionary would involve trekking into the wilds of Africa.

One of the Sisters took me round the hospital introducing me to the patients and nursing staff. It was a little embarrassing: all the Ugandans had black curly hair, cropped very short, and I struggled to distinguish the men from the women. I was introduced to many of them by name, but not being familiar with Ugandan Christian names, that didn't always help me. Still, it didn't take long for me to recognise all the different faces I came across. Fortunately, everyone I met was friendly and made me feel very welcome despite any mistakes I may have made trying to speak their language. I was eager to do my best for them.

My next test was the language. We had learned the basics on our voyage out and it had seemed very logical, but spoken with local pronunciation and intonation, it was much harder to understand. There were no translators – to prevent new arrivals, such as myself, becoming lazy in learning the local language. All the Sisters and the majority of African nurses at Nsambya did speak English, however, which made the transition easier.

Operations took place continuously, it seemed, but the ceaseless action suited me. Emergencies were frequent, especially in the maternity unit, and often the same staff had to work all day and a large portion of the night. There was no air conditioning and the theatre got very hot during the heat of the day, so we worked with the windows wide open; the windows were hung with fine mosquito netting so that at night they could keep out those insects attracted to the light of the hurricane lamps that we used in the absence of any electricity supply.

After each operation, all the theatre gowns, sheets and swabs that had been used were given to people who were employed to wash them and hang them out in the sun to dry. They were then brought in to the sterilising room, refolded and packed into drums and special containers and put into a small autoclave, which was powered by three primus stoves. The instruments were thoroughly washed, put into containers and boiled. The surgical needles were washed by the theatre staff, checked and stored in spirit, and the unopened tubes of catgut for suturing or tying off severed blood vessels were also stored in spirit.

As I became increasingly involved with delivering babies, I soon discovered there was a peculiarly high incidence of problems in childbirth. There could have been a number of reasons for this. One possibility was that many women might have had misshapen pelvises as a result of carrying heavy loads on their heads from a young age. This didn't cause them any problems or discomfort until childbirth, when it could lead to serious difficulties. Another problem was one that could occur during the birth itself: there was a highly potent African medicine that, given at the right time during labour, was very useful. However, it was often administered before the woman entered the final stages of labour, causing very painful deliveries. It was the women from the outlying villages who suffered most. Many of them arrived at Nsambya after a three-day journey being carried on a chair on the back of a bicycle over very rough roads and in severe heat. A large number of these came in with a ruptured uterus. Not only did the babies often die but, on some occasions, so did the mother. Ugandan custom dictated that a mother could not be buried with the baby inside her so in those cases where the mother died, the hospital had to conduct a post-mortem operation to remove the dead foetus. As a midwife, this sad task often fell to me and Sister Paschal who was in charge of the maternity unit.

Most of the operations we performed resembled those carried out in England, with one difference. The local people had a custom that they expected to see evidence of what happened during the operation. In practice, this meant if anything was removed from the patient as part of the surgery, the excised organ or tumour had to be put in a container and placed outside the operating theatre for the relatives to see.

The children's ward had thirty-six beds and cots but frequently was so overcrowded the children had to be nursed on mattresses on the floor. The majority of them were extremely ill – suffering from malaria, malnutrition and severe anaemia caused by intestinal parasites.

As many of our patients came from long distances, members of their family were allowed to stay at the hospital with them. There was a name for relatives who did this – *bajanjabbi*. They would arrive at the hospital armed with all their cooking pots and matoke – a green banana that was the staple diet of the majority of the people in that area. It was peeled, wrapped in banana leaves and steamed. The result resembled a soft golden potato, which was rolled into balls with fingers and dipped into a soup, usually made with peanuts – fortunately it was a meal I enjoyed, as it was regularly on the menu when I was out in the villages on safari. The *bajanjabbi* cooked all the meals for their relation, the patient, as well as for themselves. The biggest problem we had with the *bajanjabbi* was when they were told not to give food to a child who was due to have an operation. They were told that on no account should the child have anything to eat from the evening before the surgery. But regardless of this, they would get up very early on the morning of the operation, cook a meal and feed the child. This often caused difficulties for the doctor and nursing staff and led to delays in operations.

The advice I received on my arrival in Uganda turned out to be well-founded. I had been called to my first nightly emergency in the maternity ward and forgot to tuck my mosquito net under my mattress. Once I was satisfied that the mother concerned was in no danger I returned to my cubicle in our dormitory. Not only was there a huge rat sitting on my pillow, but there was an even bigger one on the washstand chewing my soap.

The soap was dark red and smelled strongly carbolic, but the rat seemed to be enjoying it. Rats are often carriers of Weil's disease, excreting the organism that causes this frequently fatal disease in their urine, so once I'd chased them out of the room I checked my bedding thoroughly for any damp patches. Had I found any, the bedding would have had to be destroyed. Fortunately everything was dry and I turned my pillow over and climbed back into bed. I remembered to tuck in my mosquito net after that – for several weeks at least.

Although it didn't fulfil my longing for rural Africa, Nsambya proved a good introduction to working in Uganda both as a nurse and a missionary. Soon, though, I was given a new appointment to a small newly built mission hospital on the borders of Uganda and Kenya. I was assured that the new mission was a long way from any large town, and was delighted to be moving out of the city and the civilisation that had so disappointed me on my arrival in Kampala. I didn't have long to dream about the new venture before I arrived.

The mission was in a very dry area with little vegetation. The hospital consisted of one large grass-roofed building with mud walls and a concrete floor. It accommodated men, women and children together. At one end of the building was a small empty room that I decided to use as a labour room. It was completely devoid of any furniture or equipment. The mission had a carpenter whom I commissioned to make a wooden bed for the new labour room; the bed had removable boards so they could be easily cleaned after each birth. Also within the compound there was a brick building that was used as a dispensary for the outpatients' treatment.

The people were a different tribe from those in Nsambya, with a different language and customs that I had to pick up. The local chiefs (called *Muluka* chiefs) held meetings with their people to inform them that medical treatment was available at the new mission. The priest also announced it at Mass on Sundays.

All the pregnant women I now saw were from small villages. Many of them had never seen or slept on a bed before coming into hospital and I had to ask the assistant midwife to get onto the bed to show them what to do for delivery. To begin with some of the women were afraid to get onto the purpose-made bed and insisted on being delivered on the floor. We didn't want to cause them unnecessary stress so we allowed this, but word soon spread that no evil had befallen mother or baby who gave birth on the bed and patients quickly accepted the way we worked.

As some of the people had to travel large distances to get to the mission, there couldn't be specific opening hours as patients might arrive at any time of the day. Many of them had never had any dealings with conventional medical treatment, only native remedies, and many were extremely ill when they arrived.

There was no antenatal care for pregnant women. Frequently they came in a poor state of health due to malaria, malnutrition and hookworm infestation, which was the main cause of anaemia.

One of my first difficulties was encouraging the women to come to the clinic regularly for examination. I began making a one-off charge of sixpence (five cents in Ugandan currency) that I refunded when they came into the hospital for their delivery. I knew this method would be successful, as the women's husbands would make sure their wives attended the hospital – if only to get their sixpence back.

I was working at the dispensary one morning when three men rushed into the compound.

'Sister!' one panted. 'You must come with us now. My wife is in labour.'

'Where is she?'

'We had to leave her. She was going to have the baby before we could reach the hospital. Please come, Sister! We'll take you to her.'

'How far away is she?'

'Very near, Sister,' they assured me.

I left an African orderly in charge of dispensing medicine and explained that I had been called to an emergency and would be back within a couple of hours. I grabbed a bag with the essentials I thought I might need to help the woman and marched off after the men.

Before long I was gasping. Although I was quite fit, it was the hottest part of the day and my white habit restricted me more than the men's light garments.

'How much further is it?' I asked.

'Only short distance.'

I continued quietly for several miles until we reached a river. There was no bridge.

'How am I to get across here?' I looked down at my long skirts.

In reply, two of the men lifted me up and carried me across. When we reached the other side, I again asked how much further we had to go.

'Not far, Sister.'

My legs were beginning to hurt, and I could feel droplets of perspiration hovering on my forehead, and running down my back. After several more miles we reached some grass-roofed huts and a large maize crop. Some of the tall stalks had been bent over and tied together forming a shelter from the sun's glare. Here, on the ground, lay the woman.

Twin boys rested naked in her arms – one was healthy but the other wasn't breathing. I knelt down and tried to resuscitate the tiny infant. I massaged his chest and laid my cheek close to his lips, to check if my efforts had had any effect. Still the baby didn't take a breath. I feared I had arrived too late to do anything. Suddenly an old lady emerged from one of the huts carrying two pieces of a broken hoe. She fell to her knees beside the apparently lifeless baby and began to bang the pieces of the hoe together, making a very loud noise. I asked her what she thought she was doing.

'Helping the baby,' she said and continued to bang.

The baby boy spluttered and then gave a shriek. I checked him over and was delighted to discover he was breathing normally. Colour came to his cheeks and lips and he soon looked as healthy as his brother.

Once he'd met his two new sons, the father insisted that we took the mother and babies to the hospital because he wanted his sixpence back. We had to retrace all the miles and the river crossing back to the mission – this time with mother and babies. On arrival, I arranged for the new mother to stay at the mission hospital overnight to recover from her exhaustion. Once I'd made sure she and the babies were being attended to, I made myself a very strong cup of tea. As I sipped it I wondered whether the Central Midwives Board in England would consider adding 'Banging together a broken hoe' to their list of approved resuscitation methods. As I laughed to myself I managed to spill my tea onto my habit.

On another occasion, at one of the bush hospitals, I had a visit from the mission's priest.

'Sister Aelred?'

'Yes, Father?'

'I wonder if you can help me. I've just had a visit from two men from one of the villages. They want me to go with them. One of them is very upset – his wife has been trying to deliver her baby for five days.'

'Of course, Father. Where are they from?'

'Their village is more than fifty miles away – they walked here. It's taken two days so I'd like to leave as soon as you can be ready.'

It was appropriate that I should accompany the priest, to offer any medical assistance I could. We set off straight away, as soon as I had put everything I thought I might need in the vehicle. The men sat in the back of the car directing us to where they lived.

When we arrived at the mud dwelling it was beginning to get dark. The priest waited outside with the other men while I went in to see what I could do. The only light came from a tiny tin container filled with paraffin with a piece of material sticking up to make a wick. Even for a nurse who had trained during wartime, the sight in that little room made my stomach turn. On the ground sat the baby's grandmother with her daughter lying between her knees; her clothes soaked red. There were pieces of baby strewn all over the floor. The poor mother opened her eyes and stared through me. She was dying.

Before I could take it all in, the baby's grandmother told me, 'The head of the baby is still inside and no one can get it out.' I nodded. I then knelt on the bloody floor and did an internal examination. The woman hardly seemed to notice. I realised that the baby had been in the womb with the feet presenting.

'What happened?' I asked the grandmother.

'When she couldn't get the baby out, her husband called the village carpenter to help. He took the baby out a piece at a time, until he got to the head – but he couldn't get that out. That was when they decided to go to the mission for help – two days ago.'

I squatted down next to the woman's mother.

'Your daughter is very ill. I'm sorry – she's not going to get better.'

The woman blinked and said nothing. She watched me, rocking her daughter, as I began to gather up the pieces of baby. I couldn't do much about cleaning the hut as the blood had soaked into the mud floor but I did what I could. I then went to call in the priest who was still waiting outside. We prayed with the mother and her daughter – it was all we could do for them. Ten minutes later the young woman died. Although it was important for the dead to be buried quickly, she could not, of course, be buried with the baby inside her. The priest asked her husband what he wanted us to do.

'Take her back with you and take what's left of the child out.' He looked past us into the darkness. Very carefully I wrapped the pieces of baby in a banana leaf and wrapped the body of the lady in an old blanket. With the priest's help, we lifted them into the car and we took them, and the husband and father, back to Nsambya, many miles away, where there were the facilities for what we had to do.

The Nsambya hospital was deathly quiet when we arrived. All of the staff were in bed. The priest helped me to transfer the woman's body from the car to the mortuary. It was important to operate quickly so I woke up the mission's doctor to do the post-mortem Caesarean section. She was sympathetic but explained that the high risk of infection would prevent her from doing other surgery. She reminded me that as a qualified midwife I was very capable of performing the operation myself. I woke up Sister Paschal to help me. Together, by the light of the hurricane lamps, we cut into the woman's abdomen to remove the baby's head. After closing the incision, we washed the mother's body and the pieces of the baby and wrapped them in clean cloth. Finally they looked peaceful.

I found the husband pacing up and down in the darkness outside. He came in with me to see his wife. His nostrils flared as he tried to hold back tears. He began pacing again, then stopped and turned to me.

'How can I get her back to the village to be buried?'

I knew how important it was in the hot climate to bury the dead quickly. When I realised it was this that was distressing him, I petitioned the priest to help again. He was still awake after the night's events – reading his Bible by lantern-light. He agreed to drive them back to their village the following morning after the church service, which he did.

It took me a long time to recover from this night. For many nights afterwards I lay awake thinking about how a healthy mother and a healthy baby could die in such a way, even though help had been sought. How many other young women in the villages watched their babies die so horribly before dying themselves in a pool of blood, I wondered. It seemed so unnecessary. The experience strengthened my resolve to do everything in my power to change this situation.

5.

Leprosy and the Touch of Love

'I wonder if any of you are free this afternoon?'

We were sitting in the refectory having our lunch with Sister Alcantara, the Superior General of our Order. She was carrying out her statutory visitation of our missions and work in Uganda and had made Nsambya her temporary headquarters during her stay. 'I need someone to drive me to Buluba. I have some business there,' she concluded.

I wasn't due to be working that afternoon and had made other plans. Through the windows of the refectory I could see the trees ruffled by the breeze. I knew that Buluba was one of our leprosy missions and that it was sixty miles away. I also knew that Sister Alcantara had damaged her ankle so couldn't drive herself. The sound of one of the African women singing floated in from the compound.

'I can do it,' I said.

I didn't mind driving. We had the windows of the car down and the cooling wind that whisked around our faces made a welcome change from the Ugandan afternoon heat (except that the open window admitted the all-pervading red dust). The journey took about two hours, so to pass the time the Superior General explained, in her lilting Irish accent, a little of the mission's history.

'Buluba Leprosy Centre – as you will soon see – stands on the bank of Thruston Bay, an inlet of Lake Victoria.'

'In Busoga district?' I asked

'That's right. In 1934, the Franciscan Missionary Sisters obtained a large area of land there, with permission to erect buildings for the treatment of leprosy. The land was completely uninhabited at that time because there had been a terrible outbreak of sleeping sickness in Busoga in the early 1900s. The disease is transmitted by the tsetse fly and these flourish in the long grass and bushes near the water that makes up half of the district. The flies were particularly rampant along the edge of Lake Victoria. Over a six-year period, more than a hundred thousand people died of sleeping sickness in Busoga and a further 6,000 died in a severe famine.'

'That many? I'm surprised there was anyone left.'

'I've heard it said that over two-thirds of the population perished. As a result, the government officials decided to relocate all the remaining population living along the lakeshore. They also cleared the bush in an attempt to eradicate the tsetse fly and mosquito from the area.'

I was about to interrupt again, but we'd reached a particularly bumpy bit of road – if you could call it that – and I had to concentrate to avoid bouncing my passenger out of the vehicle!

'Following the evacuation and clearance,' Sister Alcantara went on, 'sleeping sickness appeared to die out and, in the late 1930s, people were allowed to return to parts of the closed area. The original population of Busoga had been mainly a Bantu tribe, but large numbers of other tribes moved to the district once it was considered safe. They included people from Kenya as well as Nilotic and Hamitic tribes from neighbouring parts of

Uganda.' She smiled. 'The chiefs and local people helped dig pit latrines and collected water from the lake – just a few hundred yards from the buildings. Those initial leprosy buildings were very primitive. There was also a small temporary house for the Sisters.'

'Were you there?'

'I was,' she replied. 'I was one of the first Sisters living in that temporary house.'

We drove in silence for a few minutes. It was strange trying to picture the Superior General as an ordinary Sister like myself. But of course, I reasoned, she must have been. Before long, the history continued.

'Gradually, with generous support from overseas, it became possible to build a 32-bed hospital at Buluba with a small operating theatre. Several small houses were built for those patients who lived too far from the centre to travel for regular treatment, or who were suffering from the complications of leprosy.'

I had read about leprosy during my general medical training. It is a complex clinical condition resulting from infection with a micro-organism, Mycobacterium leprae or Hansen's Bacillus, named after the Norwegian doctor who first described it in 1873. The first known written records of the disease date from 600 BC. The disease was recognised in the ancient civilisations of China, Egypt and India. The majority of today's patients are to be found within the tropical and subtropical areas, especially where there is poverty and deprivation. Leprosy affects mainly the skin and nerves but, left untreated, can cause progressive and irreversible damage not only to these structures but also to the limbs and eyes. Although I knew the theory, I had never met anyone suffering from leprosy before. I wondered what to expect at Buluba.

'Several years ago, a permanent house was built for the Sisters, overlooking the lake, and also one for a resident priest. All the houses were built from bricks handmade by the local people and baked in a home-made kiln. Everyone who came to the centre was made welcome and received treatment and care irrespective of tribe or religion. There is now a full primary boarding school for children suffering from leprosy. They wouldn't be allowed to attend a normal school so this stops them missing out on an education. Once they are cured they can continue their learning at a normal school. There's also a farm there now with cattle and oxen and chickens, and a banana and maize plantation. The farm is tended entirely by the patients – those who are well enough to work, at least.'

I wondered if the new mission where I was stationed would ever grow in this way. I couldn't imagine it.

'Any more questions, Sister Aelred?'

'Yes – why is it called Buluba?'

'There was famous local man called Luba in the area the centre is built. It was named after him.'

When we arrived, Sister suggested that while she was carrying out her business, I should walk around the centre and talk to the patients. Immediately I was drawn to the church – a massive building standing proudly in the centre of the compound. I ran my hand along the rough handmade bricks. They were warm from the sun. Inside there was enough room for more than one hundred people. There was a strange smell in the air that I couldn't identify – I wasn't sure I wanted to. On the altar stood several vases of fresh flowers.

As I wandered further into the church I saw several women that I took to be leprosy patients, kneeling in prayer. I entered a pew and knelt down to pray also. After a few minutes, one of the ladies approached me.

'Hello, Sister. Would you like me to show you round our centre?'

'I would love that. Thank you so much.'

I followed my new friend out of the church and we were joined by another lady. As we walked towards the dormitories, squinting in the bright sun, they asked me why I'd come to Buluba.

'The big chief from Ireland has come to talk to the sister-in-charge here.' I paused. 'And I came to see you.'

My two companions exchanged a smile and then led me into their own little dormitory.

'This is our room, Sister. Do you like it?' They stood back to let me walk round the spotlessly clean room. Each bed had a locker beside and on each locker was a small vase of fresh flowers and a few modest personal belongings – a family photo, a prayer book or Bible.

I finished my inspection and turned to them. They waited in eager silence for my reaction.

'Your room is lovely – you have made it look so pretty.'

They beamed at the compliment.

'Come with us, Sister, to meet some more of the patients here.' And they took me with them to other dormitories. In one of these, I was overwhelmed by the nauseating smell, heavy, sickly and rotten. I tried to breath through my mouth but I could still taste it. A woman was perched on the edge of her bed with her back to me.

One of my guides patted her gently on the shoulder. She turned round. Her face was disfigured with several nodules and a part of her nose was missing.

'A friend has come to see us.'

The young woman smiled shyly and held out her hand. I smiled back and took the mutilated limb she offered – I had never touched anyone with leprosy before. And as my hand joined with hers, I felt such a flood of love and compassion that I had to blink away tears.

We moved on to other dormitories and I met other patients, some missing limbs and others who were blind. I shook hands with all those who offered to.

Some of the patients I met addressed me as '*Ssebo*'. I knew *Nnyabo* and *Ssebo* were the highest forms of greeting, but I'd been taught that *Ssebo* was the masculine greeting; *Nnyabo* is the feminine.

'I wish the patients would call me *Nnyabo* rather than *Ssebo*,' I complained to the ladies who were showing me round.

'Oh no!' they exclaimed. 'To be called *Ssebo* is a very great honour – it is how they would address the king!'

I realised how much dignity these people were extending to me by addressing me in this way and felt very humbled.

Finally, my companions took me to visit some of the men's dormitories. An old man, whose leprosy had made him blind in one eye, proudly showed me his home. Although the room was tiny, there were pictures hanging on the wall and a statue of the Virgin and Child on the locker. Against the far wall there was a little shelf lined with books. Like the other dormitories, it was beautifully clean and very welcoming, despite the strange smell. I was inside this miniature home when I heard my name being called. I emerged, blinking, into the sunlight to find Sister Alcantara standing by the car, ready to leave.

'Goodbye, my friends. I'm so grateful to you for your kindness and for showing me your homes here.'

'Goodbye, Sister. Come back to see us again,' they replied as I climbed into the driving seat. As we pulled away, I was touched by how many of Buluba's residents waited to wave us off. I saw in the mirror that many of the hands in the air were heavily bandaged.

Once the mission was out of sight, I pressed Sister Alcantara to continue the Buluba history lesson.

Meeting some of its residents had aroused my curiosity.

'Were you there from the beginning, Sister?' I asked her.

'I was.'

'What was it like?'

'Well my dear,' she smiled, 'opening day was a bit of a shock! Previously, we had asked the *Muluka* chiefs to encourage those people suffering from leprosy to attend the centre for treatment. We'd been open an hour and we soon realised from the influx of people that the chiefs had rounded up every single person they *thought* might have leprosy. Hundreds of people arrived – some disabled, blind, deformed, some with huge suppurating ulcers, and many with all kinds of other illnesses. People had to wait a long time, but by the end of the day everyone had received some kind of help. As you know, at this time there was still no known cure for leprosy, so all we did was put chaulmoogra oil on their lesions and clean and dress the ulcers – if they were really bad, it took more than an hour to treat one patient. Of course, by the end of that first day, we were exhausted. And you know what stigma there is attached to leprosy now?'

I nodded. I knew that people were more frightened of leprosy than almost any other condition.

'Well, it was even worse then. Many of the people we saw had been ostracised by their families.'

'Why are they so afraid of it?'

'They don't think of it as a disease. They believe it's caused by the spirit of a dead relative. When a person dies of leprosy, the relatives put a bunch of bananas and a gourd of beer into the grave to feed the spirit. They take it very seriously. Often the sufferers themselves don't view their disease as a medical condition but as a punishment from the spirit of an ancestor for some misdeed. And because they haven't received treatment, many of them lose the use of one or more of their limbs.'

I didn't know how to reply.

We drove along in silence for a few miles. I've no idea what Sister Alcantara was thinking about but I was praying, 'Dear Lord, please don't ever let me be appointed to this place.'

It became cooler on the way back to the mission. Sister Alcantara quizzed me on my impressions of Buluba. Until visiting the centre, I hadn't met a leprosy patient and certainly hadn't realised the extent of their suffering – it had shocked me. I couldn't help mentioning the smell that seemed to permeate everywhere. She explained that it was caused by a mixture of chaulmoogra oil (used on the leprosy lesions to alleviate discomfort and to darken the affected areas of skin, so making the lesions less obvious) and pus from the discharging ulcers some of the patients had.

'There was something else I noticed. Why were there no African doctors or nurses there?'

'They are frightened, Sister. No African – even among the medical professionals – will work with leprosy. If a leprosy patient went to an ordinary government medical centre they would be sent away.'

About a week later, the Superior General sent for me.

'Sister Aelred.'

'Good morning, Sister Alcantara.'

She ruffled some papers that were in front of her, and then looked straight at me.

'I've called you here to tell you that you've been appointed to Buluba Leprosy Centre.'

I couldn't meet her gaze. I shuffled my weight from one foot to the other trying to ignore the sick feeling deep in the pit of my stomach.

'Do I have to? I mean – I'm very happy here – is there no one else?'

She frowned. 'I'm sorry, Sister, someone has already been appointed to your post here.'

'Thank you, Sister.' I didn't trust myself to say anything else. I dipped my head and hurried out. I sat in my room with my Bible open, but I couldn't read it. I'd told God I didn't want to go there. After some time spent on my own, thinking and praying, I felt calmer. I knew the move to Buluba wasn't open to debate so it was important to prepare myself for my new role and new home as best I could. I was sad to leave my current post, but I was determined to trust God – I prayed this move was part of his plan.

When I arrived back in Buluba, this time as a member of staff, I received an affectionate welcome from both the other Sisters and the leprosy patients.

In my first year, we had as many as 300 resident leprosy patients at any one time. There were a large proportion of long-term residents. This was partly due to our primary boarding school, which accounted for 100 children aged four to twelve. Some of our patients would never leave Buluba because of blindness or a permanent disability caused by severe leprosy. We didn't have enough provision for a secondary school, so children still suffering from leprosy after the age of twelve could not continue their education, unless they could be cured.

One hot February day during my first dry season at Buluba, I was sitting by an enormous stretch of raging water on the west bank of the River Nile. I could feel the heat from the rock on my legs even through my nursing coat. Sister Alcantara had brought me with her to Jinja to buy some cloth and other supplies for Buluba. Jinja was the nearest sizeable town to the leprosy centre and was the source of most of our supplies. There were a lot of *dukkas* (small shops) that sold a variety of different things; we could always find what we were looking for in one of them. Once we'd purchased everything we needed, we had some time to spare, so Sister Alcantara offered to show me another part of Lake Victoria, just outside the town. The water here was far more violent than that of the peaceful Thruston Bay, but no less beautiful. I sat mesmerised as it rushed past us – enjoying its cooling spray in the afternoon heat. A crested crane flew high above us, making its peculiar call '*Ngali, ngali*'. The bird has become the symbol of Uganda, pictured on the national flag. The people call it *Ngali* after the cry it makes. Of Uganda's 900 species of bird, the crested crane is one of my favourites. After it had gone, a silence descended – no sound except the water, gushing past the rocks.

'You've heard of the Ripon Falls?' Sister Alcantara asked.

'Yes.'

'That's what we're looking at.'

I realised suddenly that I was confronted with the same scene that John Hanning Speke had seen and written of in July 1862. I knew from my history lessons that Speke was the first explorer to correctly identify the source of the River Nile as Lake Victoria, and that the Nile leaves Lake Victoria at the Ripon Falls. (These falls were completely submerged in 1954 by the Owen Falls dam.) Speke had been a man of tremendous courage and commitment – he had overcome many dangers and difficulties in realising his ambition to find the Nile's source. These thoughts began to make me feel differently about being posted to Buluba. My journey to Africa had been more than just a physical one – I wondered what discoveries still lay in store for me.

Evening was approaching as we walked back to the centre of Jinja. The first stars were just beginning to peep from the swiftly darkening sky. I was looking forward to dinner and my bed back at the mission. Then, Sister Alcantara stopped abruptly.

'What is it, Sister?'

'Can you see that?'

I peered into the dusk. I could just make out something moving near the river – something big.

'What is that?'

'Shhh!' She didn't turn to me, but kept her eyes fixed on whatever it was. 'Just be patient, Sister,' she murmured, motionless.

As we watched, a hippopotamus lumbered up from the riverbank and onto the street, twenty metres in front of us. I turned to Sister Alcantara, who was smiling and looking towards the river. I held my breath and followed her gaze. Emerging from the gloom was another of these beasts – even bigger than the first, if that was possible. He flung open his mouth in an enormous yawn and clumped after his companion.

'Are they safe?' I whispered.

'As long as you don't get between them and the river.'

I frowned. Our car was parked about half a mile in the direction the animals had taken. If we followed them, even at a distance, we might find ourselves between them and the river. Sister must have read my thoughts.

'It's OK,' she assured me. 'We'll just have to go the long way round.'

I learned that this sight was not uncommon on the streets of Jinja. The hippos weren't bothered about the people and the people weren't bothered about the hippos – providing they gave each other a wide enough berth.

Over time, the Sister-in-charge of Buluba's farm decided to expand. She bought turkeys, encouraged by the thought of more meat and larger eggs, but the birds proved extremely hard to rear. Undeterred, the Sister organised the planting of sugar cane as a cash crop. Initially, the income was for the patients' pocket money, but it yielded enough to make the centre almost self-supporting.

It also became possible to recruit a doctor. Dr Wanda Blenska arrived at Buluba in 1951. She came to us from Poland. She had a firm handshake and bright blue eyes that smiled before her mouth did. I warmed to her instantly. Her arrival coincided with that of a new drug from America: diaminodiphenyl sulphone (dapsone or DDS as it became known) revolutionised the treatment of leprosy. Buluba was one of the first leprosy centres in the world to use it. Given weekly as oral tablets, it opened up the opportunity for treatment of patients many miles away who couldn't travel to Buluba.

The more I got to know Wanda, the more I liked and admired her. She was a prayerful woman, and her evident love of Jesus spilled out into every aspect of her life. Not only was our new doctor popular with me, but with the patients too. She treated them with such gentleness and courtesy. One April morning, I was standing in the compound with two of our long-term residents, one of whom was blind and severely mutilated. It was one of those rare dry mornings in the midst of the long rains and we were enjoying the fresh air before the next downpour. Wanda paused to greet us and have a chat before going to the wards to see her patients. After she'd left us, one of the women said, 'Oh, how that woman loves us!'

'Yes,' the blind one agreed. 'She carries the perfume of Jesus.'

6.

From Pyjamas to Birthday Suits

About four years after my arrival at Buluba, Sister Alcantara was appointed the Sister-in-charge. She was a woman of vision; I hoped and anticipated significant progress in the treatment of leprosy under her guidance.

Christmas preparations began early for the mission staff at Buluba. All of the patients with leprosy, and their families if they were residents, were given new clothes as presents. The men were allowed to choose one pair of long or short khaki trousers and a long or short-sleeved shirt. The ladies could have either a dress or a traditional *gayaza*. The boys were given short khaki trousers and a shirt, while each girl received a pretty dress.

So, as early as the previous July, we went to the town of Jinja to visit the *dukkas*. These were owned, predominantly, by the Asian community, and imported beautiful materials from India as well as other commodities, from boiled sweets to scented soap. Once we had bought all the materials, cottons and buttons we needed, the sewing began in earnest. We taught those patients who were physically able how to sew by hand and use a sewing machine so they could help with the task. Once the sewing was complete, each garment was pressed, folded and made into a parcel, with the individual's name on a Christmas card put onto it. During the year we often received gifts from overseas benefactors, and we saved anything suitable such as toys, jewellery or clothes for the Christmas parcels. Each adult also received a packet of tea, sugar, salt, soap, biscuits and cigarettes (cigarettes would hardly be considered suitable hospital gifts nowadays!). The children were each given a packet of sweets and a piece of soap. Families also received a bunch of matoke and a piece of beef so that they could cook Christmas dinner for themselves.

One year, we received a huge consignment of gifts from the USA including dozens of pairs of pyjamas in an array of colours and patterns. We decided to put a pair in each of the men's parcels. On Christmas Eve, we distributed the parcels amongst much laughter and dancing. Sister Alcantara explained to the men that their pyjamas were not like their other clothes, and were only to be worn at night. That evening, we arrived at church for the Midnight Service to a scene of intoxicating colour and fragrance. All the ladies were wearing their new clothes and each had made a corsage from the heavily perfumed, waxy-flowered frangipani shrubs that grew so profusely in the compound. Frangipani flowers and bamboo were spread over the altar – and all the men were proudly dressed in their new pyjamas.

In the weeks leading up to Christmas, a huge crib scene had been built outside the church, with life-sized figures of Mary and Joseph with the baby Jesus and the watching animals. Towards the end of the joyous Midnight Mass, one of the congregation had been instructed to go outside and light dozens of candles around the crib so that it seemed to glow in the darkness.

I watched as everyone knelt to pray. Some were blind, some without fingers or toes; others were covered in nodules or had fallen-in noses. As the candles flickered over their smiles and the stars above them glittered, I felt awestruck at the beauty of the scene I was witnessing. And when they stood up and started to sing the Christmas carols, many of their voices destroyed by leprosy, I was moved to tears. I believed that Jesus was very real to each one of them, and that he wrapped them all in his love. It was one of those precious moments that I will continue to thank God for – the perfect end to a wonderful evening. It may seem strange, but I think a leprosy centre is one of the happiest places to be at Christmas time.

The following morning, when Sister Alcantara pretended to remonstrate with the men for wearing their pyjamas to Midnight Mass, they insisted that Sister herself had told them to wear them only at night. Exactly what they had done!

During my time at Buluba and my previous posts, I often met with an assumption that birds existed only to be captured, skewered, roasted and eaten. I understood this was an African custom, but I wanted to teach the children, at least, that birds could also be enjoyed alive. With this in mind, I instructed the building of an aviary made from wood and chicken wire and bought seven budgerigars. I showed the children how to look after them – a task they enjoyed very much. In fact, each of them was so eager to fill the containers with seed and water that I had to organise a timetable to avoid squabbles breaking out. I told the children that God liked the birds and that was why he made them so beautiful.

Not long after the budgies arrived, there was a terrible squawking and screeching in the compound. I went to check the aviary but the budgies were fine. I followed the sound round to the back of the school and saw a beautifully coloured bird being attacked by some other birds. I rushed over, clapping my hands together and shouting until the birds flew off leaving their victim on the ground. I scooped up the heap of quivering green, red and black feathers and realised I was holding a turaco from the Belgian Congo. It must have been blown off course. Evidently it wouldn't survive left to the mercy of Uganda's native birds so, after checking it hadn't been too badly damaged, I put it in the aviary with the budgies. It was a lot bigger than its new companions, with a crest on its head and a long parrot-like tail. I monitored the birds initially as I wasn't sure how either species would react to the other, but they all seemed to get on. It was a privilege to see such a beautiful bird at close range – for the children and for myself.

Several weeks later, I was in the church when two Africans rushed in, their eyes wide.

'*Nnyabo*, come! There's a snake and he's eating the eggs of the budgies and he's killing all the budgies. You must come!'

I hurried after them to the other side of the compound. A huddle of spectators were pointing and shrieking. A small snake's head protruded through the chicken wire. He had clearly feasted on the eggs, as the resulting bulge was what was keeping him trapped within the aviary. He was vomiting up the eggshells onto the ground, trying to escape.

'Kill it, *Nnyabo*. Kill the snake!' The children shouted in unison.

'No.'

I made the children stand aside – even a small snake could have enough venom to kill or cause serious illness to a human. We watched until the serpent had digested enough of his meal to squeeze through the chicken wire and skulk away into the long grass.

The Kingdom of Buganda, like the rest of Uganda, had become a British Protectorate in 1894 and was still under British administration at the time of the coronation of Queen Elizabeth II in 1953. Although the Ugandans could have been excused for a lack of interest in the monarch of their ruling power, they did, in fact, appear genuinely excited about the coronation of the young queen, Elizabeth – not least because there would be widespread official celebrations. Several days prior to the coronation, every schoolchild received a commemorative medal to wear at the various festivities that were held to mark the event.

As our bush mission on the Ugandan border with Kenya (where I temporarily worked as a locum) had a well-established school that was large enough to accommodate all the expected guests, the government officials selected it as the venue for celebrations for the whole area. Local people helped to erect within our compound a large shelter, covered with a grass roof, to house all the official dignitaries who would be attending. There was a sense of anticipation surrounding the preparations that seemed to be felt across the country. It intensified until the day finally arrived, and the mood of everyone was one of sheer merriment. The various *Muluka* chiefs arranged for lorries to collect schoolchildren from the outlying villages and bring them to the mission. Many of them arrived weary from their journey and coated with a layer of red dust. They perked up after they had washed themselves at the large water tanks and changed into their various school uniforms. Before the celebrations began officially, the children received a meal of meat and matoke, followed by some free time. As they played games and tried not to get their uniforms dirty, another lorry arrived bringing the police band. They emerged from the lorry clad in khaki uniforms, with navy puttees – strips of cloth that coiled from the top of their shining boots to their knees – and each wore a navy fez. They arranged their instruments, tuned up and began to play, as the official representatives arrived and the children lined up ready for the march past.

Finally, the District Officer – the Queen's representative at the event – arrived with his entourage. Quickly, he took his place with the other dignitaries under the newly built shelter. The march past began, school by school. I smiled to myself as our own bush mission children marched by in their cream and tomato-red uniforms, each proudly wearing the coronation medal.

The procession paused as each school reached the District Officer and other dignitaries. The children then sang a song they had prepared for the occasion. One of the schools, instead of singing, presented the District Officer with a brightly decorated cow. I heard some stifled snorts from the shelter as the assembled officials tried to hide their amusement, but he received the gift with great courtesy.

At the rear of the procession was a group of boys aged between five and twelve years. They were from a bush school and completely naked bar one item. Each boy had the centre vein from a banana leaf looped round his waist. And to each banana vein was tied the commemorative medal. I thought it showed great enterprise! As this school reached the shelter, the boy at the front said (in English), 'Eyes wight.' At this, the boys stopped marching, turned their heads and, in unison, saluted the District Officer. He had now been standing and saluting for more than an hour and I observed that this time his saluting hand was trembling with suppressed laughter.

The official guests were given refreshments while the children changed out of their uniforms and were given another meal before climbing into the lorries to be transported back to their villages. It was strange to be celebrating an event that was happening thousands of miles away in England. I'd been in Uganda for six years and I couldn't decide which country now felt more like home.

At one of our bush missions, we had to rely on the local people for our basic supplies such as milk, eggs, sweet potatoes and maize. Every morning a man called Lukongo brought our milk to us. He lived five miles away and would carry the gourd of milk on his head supported by a ring of grass. It was the custom in that region for the carriers of goods to sing as they went along – announcing to anyone and everyone what they were carrying and where they were going.

Although the milk was supposed to be high in butter-fat levels, it always looked a watery, almost bluish colour. After several days of watery milk, we asked Lukongo if he was adding water to the milk, but he assured us he would never do such a thing. After he'd gone we always boiled the milk to ensure it was safe to drink.

One morning as Lukongo was pouring the milk from its container into our cooking pot, a tiny frog fell out. Sister Bernadette scooped up the frog and held it in front of Lukongo.

'I knew you were putting water into the milk, and this,' she said, waggling the frog, 'proves it!'

Lukongo put his head on one side. He leant forward to examine the frog, and then took a step back, scratching his head. Slowly, a grin spread across his face,

'No, *Nnyabo*. I know what it is – when I was walking the cows home last night, I let them drink in the river and that must be how the frog got into the milk.'

I noticed Sister Bernadette blink twice, and then she laughed. 'Be off with you!'

As Lukongo scuttled out of the room, I turned to her and raised my eyebrows.

'What else could I say?' she sighed.

I'd been in Uganda thirteen years when it was decided that priests and nuns who were missionaries should return to their home country every few years to benefit both their physical and spiritual health. Some of the Sisters I knew had been in Uganda so long that they had lost their parents and anybody they would have wanted to see at home, so they decided to stay. I was thrilled that I'd have an opportunity to see my parents again, but I had to wait my turn. Although I was excited when the time arrived, it was strange returning to England; everything seemed to have changed – or perhaps it was me who had changed? Mother was so proud of me: when we went to Sunday Mass on the Wirral, she announced to everyone she knew, 'Come and meet my daughter. She's home from Africa after thirteen years!'

I silently begged her to stop. I had no conversation for anybody – I felt strangely unfamiliar with England and its people, and sometimes found myself using the vernacular Luganda language when replying to questions from my parents' friends. Africa was now my true home.

7.

Leprosy Control – the Dream Becomes Reality

During the early 1950s, Dr Kinnear Brown, the special leprologist to the government, carried out a number of sample surveys in conjunction with Dr Wanda Blenska and me. After initial trials at Buluba, we knew that the new drug, DDS, had the potential to revolutionise the treatment of leprosy. We had to explore the possibility of reaching more patients in outlying villages, many miles from Buluba. To do this, though, we would need properly trained staff with transport. It was an exciting opportunity but one which needed careful planning. There was another leprosy centre in Teso, 300 miles north of Buluba, run by the Church Missionary Society. It was called Kumi. With encouragement and support from Sister Alcantara, I contacted our Church Missionary Society colleagues at Kumi. They too had realised the possibilities of DDS treatment and told me of their plans to start a training school for leprosy assistants. They had already begun to set up a village treatment system throughout the Teso district with the aim of treating people from a wider area. On the basis of this, and as a result of our sample surveys, it was decided that we could emulate this system in Busoga.

This new venture would involve two aspects: firstly, the building of villages specifically for leprosy patients within Busoga district and secondly, the training of Ugandan nationals as leprosy assistants to live in the villages permanently. A subsidiary benefit was that of broadening leprosy education: dispelling some of the myths and fears that surrounded the disease. Again with Sister Alcantara's encouragement, Dr Blenska and I approached the Uganda Medical Department for permission to open a school for young men to train as leprosy assistants. We prayed that our request would be granted, and indeed it was, but the department was unable to assist with paying any salaries. This didn't prove to be a problem as the support we enjoyed from our overseas benefactors enabled us to pay the leprosy assistants a salary of twenty shillings a month and provide them with a bicycle. Twenty Ugandan shillings were equivalent to about one British pound. While the assistants were in training their uniforms, board and lodging would be free. Dr Blenska and I then had a meeting with Dr Maurice Lea and Sister Mary Stone, our counterparts at Kumi. Together, we worked out a joint syllabus for a two-year training course. This meant the leprosy assistant students at both schools would be following the same training course and could have a joint exam.

The work was the beginning of a wonderful Christian friendship between the two leprosy centres – the first truly ecumenical movement in Uganda. Those of us who are still alive remain very close friends more than fifty years later.

Dr Kadama, the Chief Medical Officer, was at that time the District Medical Officer for Busoga, and it was due to his enthusiasm that the first villages for leprosy patients were built. Instructed by the *Muluka* chiefs, the local people built small one-roomed mud houses with grass roofs and pit latrines for themselves, and a small house with a kitchen for a resident leprosy assistant. They also built another small house that could be used as a dispensary. An open shelter was attached to the dispensary to ensure privacy for the patients when they were being examined. Once the building work was finished, all the houses were whitewashed inside and out, creating an inviting little village.

The training in Buluba began in 1956. Dr Blenska and I were to be the main tutors for the two-year programme. Our first students were a small group of young men who had volunteered for the course. We were delighted that six of them were themselves ex-leprosy patients – this in itself was a significant achievement because of the terrible fear attached to leprosy. Even in the few short years I had been stationed at Buluba, it felt as though considerable progress had been made.

By January 1960 there were twelve leprosy villages, catering for both residents and outpatients. From these villages, the resident leprosy assistant was encouraged to go amongst the population and into the local schools, to talk to the chiefs and people, including children, educating them about leprosy and where they could go for diagnosis and treatment. By this time, our sponsorship from overseas donors in England and Germany meant that we had been able to provide the leprosy assistants with motorbikes. This extended the distance they could travel from the village so most of Busoga district could be covered.

Part of my work at this time was to visit each leprosy village every month, examine anyone suspected of having leprosy and initiate treatment in those with confirmed disease. The leprosy assistant then continued the treatment. Skin ulcers, which are common in leprosy sufferers, were cleansed and dressed, and patients were given lessons in the care of their hands and feet. This was necessary as the leprosy affected the peripheral nerves, which meant that sufferers might have no sensation in their feet or their fingers. Many of those suffering from leprosy would cook on an open fire and would lift the handle-less pot with their bare hands or would pick up a piece of charcoal that had fallen from the fire and put it back under the pot with their fingers. They couldn't feel the burns they suffered so they wouldn't get treatment, leaving them to go septic. In severe cases, a person's fingertips would start to resorb giving the impression that they had no fingers. One simple lesson we taught them was if they did get burned, to go and get treatment for it immediately. The nerve damage could also affect their mobility so we encouraged patients to practise particular exercises that would prevent their hands and feet becoming clawed.

During this period I spent much of my time visiting the various leprosy villages and holding clinics. Many of the patients I saw didn't wear shoes. They'd walk on stones and thorns, injuring their feet, but wouldn't feel any pain owing to the nerve damage. Some patients would arrive at the clinic with ulcers so deep that you could put your whole hand into the sole of their foot. We received generous donations from America of hand-knitted white cotton bandages. There was never any shortage of them: every time a ship came in we'd be given a sack-load. We would carefully dress the patient's foot with one of these bandages with the instructions: 'When this one gets dirty, take it off and replace it with a clean one.' And I would present them with a spare bandage to take home. In a month or so when they returned to the clinic, they would once again be barefooted and would proudly produce the clean bandage. It was very frustrating, as the wounds would never heal under these conditions. Even before I arrived at Buluba, the occupational therapist had made sandals for the patients from old car tyres, salvaged from the local garages. In the beginning the tyres were cut up with a sharp knife, which was hard work, but then someone managed to get hold of an old clog-making knife from Lancashire. This had a massive blade that had to be fastened to the floor so it could be used safely. The therapist was able to cut properly shaped soles for sandals. With the help of the patients, straps were attached to the soles and wearable pairs of sandals were produced. This proved an inspired idea. The patients were delighted to receive the sandals and were much more likely to wear them all the time than their bandages.

It wasn't just leprosy that I came across: there were many other diseases that required medical attention such as malaria, malnutrition, hookworm and other parasites, tuberculosis and 'wasting disease'.[1] If any of the people that I encountered at a treatment session needed hospital treatment, whether as an inpatient or an outpatient, I would take them back to Buluba with me. In order to be a resident in the treatment village, a patient had to meet certain criteria, such as having a long distance to travel for regular treatment; severe ulcers that needed daily dressing; or multibacillary leprosy. (Leprosy was classified as multibacillary when the patient had multiple lesions typical of leprosy and leprosy bacilli were found on microscopic examination of skin smears. Patients with this form of leprosy were more likely to be contagious to other susceptible people, and were likely to require many years of treatment.) In the treatment village, patients looked after themselves and were given plots of land to grow their own food. They were also allowed to have their families living with them. It was a privilege to be part of the same ministry as Jesus; not only did he heal people, he gave value to those being shunned by society. These leprosy villages enabled those who had been ostracised to live as part of a community, as well as have treatment for their disease.

As more leprosy assistants qualified it was possible to establish peripheral units for outpatients, the aim being that no patient should have to walk more than five miles for treatment. We had found that a long journey was the main reason for patient non-attendance. Since no buildings were required for these units, I would consult the *Muluka* chief of that area, and together we would decide an appropriate venue for the sessions. Sometimes they would take place in the compound of a chief or a patient, the marketplace, a school playing field, or even under a tree; indeed, anywhere where a number of people gathered. We called these peripheral units 'aid posts'. The Leprosy Control Officer visited the aid posts regularly to examine new patients, confirm diagnosis and discuss treatment with the leprosy assistant. It was then up to the leprosy assistant to arrange the day and time when they would attend the aid post to distribute treatment.

Travelling to different parts of Busoga meant interacting with different tribes. There are about twenty-eight distinct tribes in Uganda: each with its own language and customs. Any member of these groups is fiercely protective of others in the tribe and will fight, even to the death, to protect one of their own. During my monthly clinic at one of the village medical centres, a little boy came for treatment. He marched up to the table where I was sitting and flung himself down on the chair opposite. He wished me 'Good morning' and announced his name. He looked about five years old. As I wrote his name in the register, smiling to myself, I spoke to him.

'You're a Mugandan, aren't you?'

His chair scraped along the floor as he jumped to his feet and clenched his fists, blowing out his cheeks.

'No. I'm a Musoga!'

Immediately I apologised for my mistake and offered him a sweet, which he refused – such was the degree of his disgust.

As I met the child on subsequent visits to this village, I remembered he was a Musoga. Gradually his anger subsided and we became friends.

The workload and responsibilities of the leprosy assistants steadily increased so that the initial syllabus we had developed in consultation with Kumi didn't cover all that was needed. We updated the course so that in the first year it included anatomy and physiology, health science, practical nursing, first aid and an introduction to leprosy and physiotherapy. The second year consisted of leprosy diagnosis, treatment and control, statistics, health education and tropical diseases. In the 1960s, as a result of the increased demands, the standard of education required for those who wanted to train as leprosy assistants was raised to that of Senior Secondary 3 or higher.

Each second-year leprosy assistant spent one month in residence at a treatment centre with a senior leprosy assistant and accompanied me, in my capacity as the Leprosy Control Officer, on my routine visits to the centres. Our desire was that leprosy treatment would eventually be incorporated in the Ugandan general medical service. Even among the medical professionals, the spiritual connotations of having leprosy meant that sufferers were still feared and marginalised – shunned by ordinary hospitals. With this in mind we chose suitable leprosy assistants, who had qualified on our two-year programme, to train as general nurses or laboratory assistants at Nsambya Nurse Training School in Kampala – where I had (to my dismay) been appointed on arriving in Africa.

Between January 1960 and December 1969, fifty-eight students successfully passed the examination and were awarded the Certificate of the Ugandan Medical Department. Some were sent to work in other districts in Uganda; two were trained for Geita district in Tanzania and four for Kenya. Qualified leprosy assistants in Busoga and indeed the whole of Uganda were given regular annual refresher courses at Buluba or one of the district centres. We felt particularly blessed when those who applied to be leprosy assistants were former patients. Some of them we hadn't seen since they were children; they had attended our primary school, but had gone on to finish their education at an ordinary secondary school after being cured.

Buluba became known as a Centre of Excellence for leprosy treatment, not only locally but also in many countries worldwide.

Living and working in Africa, we often had experiences that were heart-stopping in retrospect; at the time, we just had to deal with the situation in the best way we knew and didn't have time to think or be frightened.

I never remember Dr Blenska appearing scared of anything, save for one Sunday, when she was returning to Buluba after an afternoon's recreation. She had a small kayak that she liked to take out into Thruston Bay, enjoying the peace and the break from her work, quietly paddling back and forth. On this particular afternoon I met her just as she was coming off the water, carrying the kayak, with the paddle abandoned in the grass further away. Her face was pale and she was sweating. It didn't take all my training to know that she was in shock

'Whatever is the matter, Wanda?' I asked.

She pointed back to the lake. 'I'd paddled out as far as that inlet, when a crocodile started to chase me.'

We all knew that it was not unknown for crocodiles to chase and kill fishermen out on the lake. I walked down to the water's edge to collect the paddle and we trudged in silence for a short distance. Dr Blenska suddenly stopped and, turning to me, said gravely, 'Sister, I could see its tonsils.'

At that I burst out laughing. 'Come on,' I said. 'Let's go and make a cup of tea.'

It took some time for Dr Blenska to get over her fright and I don't think she ever ventured out on this part of the lake again in her kayak.

On some occasions I would stay overnight at a leprosy village, particularly if it was a long distance from Buluba. If I had travelled there on a Saturday, it meant I could visit the local church for Mass the following morning. As many as several hundred people might attend. (In 1963 the services ceased to be in Latin and were instead conducted in the local languages, which made them more accessible.) Some of the congregation would walk as far as ten miles to reach the church, often pausing to sleep en route. Most of these churches were built very simply and did not have seats. The people usually sat on the floor, men on one side, women and children on the other. The mothers of babies breastfed during the service, while their other children sat quietly, always very well behaved. These people were poor, so when the collection plate was passed round, they put in eggs, many of which had been saved up for a while. They didn't regard the eggs as a substitute for money, but simply as a gift to the priest. At the end of a service he had more eggs than he could eat so he would often send his surplus eggs to the Sisters. Many of the eggs were old or had been carried in the heat for a couple of days before they arrived at church, so we had to throw the bad ones away. There may have been two usable eggs in every dozen we received. Of course, we would never tell those who gave them that they were unusable; in their poverty, the eggs were a very generous gift.

As part of our commitment to seeing the treatment of leprosy integrated into the general medical service, we continued to think of ways to distribute information about leprosy and to dispel some of the myths that surrounded it. Perhaps inspired by the Coronation day celebrations, we decided to hold a parole ceremony at Buluba for our cured patients and invite as many dignitaries and others as possible. We prepared certificates that would be presented to each cured patient. We had never given out certificates before but we wanted to emphasise the importance of attending a leprosy centre for regular treatment.

I knew where the *Saza* chief of Buluba lived, so I went to visit him. The *Saza* chiefs are in charge of a whole district – a level above the *Gombolola* chiefs and two above the *Muluka* chiefs. If you have a *Saza* chief behind you, you can do almost anything. After a warm greeting, the chief invited me into his home. I asked him if he would be prepared to host a meeting with some of the other *Saza* chiefs so we could tell them about our parole ceremony. He agreed, and the following week we were able to ask all the *Saza* chiefs present if they could organise the transport of all the recently cured leprosy patients to Buluba. Approximately three hundred people were due to be discharged.

As this was the first ceremony of its kind, we wanted a special dignitary to present certificates to the discharged patients. I approached the *Kyabazinga* (king) of Busoga – Sir William Wilberforce Nadiope. He didn't need persuading – he was delighted to do this for his people. We also invited Dr Kadama, the Chief Medical Officer for Uganda (himself a member of the Basoga tribe), some local doctors, medical assistants and nurses, as well as civil dignitaries.

A week before the parole ceremony, I was in Kampala buying the monthly supplies. I'd bought all I needed for the journeys I'd be making to the various villages that month and was on my way to meet up with the Sister who was buying supplies for Buluba. As I passed the window of the Bata Shoe Company shop, a thought struck me. I decided I should go inside and ask if I could have a word with the manager. I introduced myself to the man behind the till and explained what I wanted. I didn't have to wait long before the manager appeared from a back room and greeted me. He told one of his staff to look after my things and led me up to his office, where I began to tell him about the parole ceremony. He seemed very interested, which gave me courage to pursue the idea that had brought me into the shop in the first place.

'*Ssebo*, I wonder if it would be at all possible for your company to donate some shoes to give to the people being paroled – as a little gift for persevering with their treatment.'

He paused and put his head on one side. 'I don't see why not. How many pairs of shoes do you want?'

I flushed slightly. 'Well, *Ssebo*, we have about three hundred men, women and children, but I have no idea of sizes.'

He laughed – a deep throaty laugh – the sort that causes its hearers to smile. 'Don't you worry, *Nnyabo*,' he said. 'I will send out a mixture and, if they don't fit, send them back and I will change them for you.'

'Thank you, *Ssebo*,' I said, rising from my chair.

'In fact, I'll give you 400 – then you'll have some spare for the next ceremony!' He laughed again but I knew he was serious.

I walked out of the shop beaming.

A few days before the ceremony, local people began constructing large shelters from grass and chairs were brought from the mission for the VIPs. From 5 a.m. on the morning of the ceremony day, lorries began to arrive, carrying those who were going to be paroled, and their relatives. By 10 a.m. everyone had arrived – more than a thousand people milling around the compound.

The police band played and the VIP guests began to arrive. Just before midday there were a few moments of quiet anticipation; then, at twelve noon exactly, His Excellency the *Kyabazinga* and his entourage appeared. There were cheers and applause and drum thumping. The band played the national anthem and the ceremony began.

I had prepared a speech giving the facts about leprosy – that it could be cured with the right treatment and that it needn't be so feared. It was an ideal opportunity to present accurate information about leprosy, particularly as many chiefs and people from the Ministry of Health were in attendance. As my turn to speak approached I smoothed the paper between my hands. I had diligently written down the whole thing in the Luganda language. As my name was announced I tossed the paper onto my chair – I wanted to speak from memory. I stood and smiled at the hundreds of Africans standing before me. My speech began 'Open your ears to what I am going to say . . .' The Luganda word for ears is very similar to their word for teeth. I took a breath and began, but I made a mistake – instead of inviting them to open their ears, as I had written on my paper, I accidentally invited the crowd to open their teeth!

As soon as I'd said it, I realised my error. No one corrected me. The crowd listened in respectful silence – no one so much as sniggered. I caught Sister Alcantara's eye. She was glaring at me, and I could understand why; if I'd just read what I'd written, I wouldn't have made the mistake. I took a deep breath and continued. The other speeches passed in something of a blur as I wondered what Sister Alcantara would say to me afterwards.

At the end of the ceremony, the *Kyabazinga* was responding to those who had spoken. He turned to me and said, with complete sincerity, 'And Sister, thank you very much for taking the trouble to learn our language.' Everyone clapped enthusiastically. And, despite my embarrassment, I appreciated his courtesy.

After this the *Kyabazinga* presented the certificates, taking time to say something to each discharged patient. The manager of the Bata Shoe Company distributed a pair of shoes to everyone who had received a certificate. As there wasn't time to try on the shoes, they were given a pair each and told to sort them out later between themselves. Sister Alcantara, who had by now forgiven my mistake, sat with me at the meal. We laughed together as we watched the paroled patients trying on the shoes and making sure they fitted properly – this seemed more important to them than the lovely meal that had been prepared in their honour before they returned to their homes.

After the usual entertainment of dancing, and singing along with the band, the transport lorries filled with happy, healthy people wearing new shoes and big smiles. The VIPs commented on how uplifting and informative the ceremony had been. I hoped and prayed that the word would spread that leprosy could be cured with regular treatment and care.

8.

Lightning Strikes Twice

'*Nnyabo, Nnyabo*!'

I woke with a jolt.

'*Nnyabo*, we need you to come – it's the pregnant lady – you said to wake you if there were any problems.'

'Yes, yes,' I said, pulling on my coat and boots, 'I'm coming.'

As I walked the quarter of a mile from the staff house to the maternity unit, I could hear the hippos grazing near the lake. It was common for them to come out of the water at night to feed on the grass. I helped deliver the baby and, once I was satisfied mother and baby would manage the rest of the night without me, I planned to return to my bed. I was on duty in the operating theatre that morning and I needed my sleep. As I stood at the door of the maternity unit I could make out shapes in the darkness. Some of the hippos had come right up to the buildings and were grazing yards away from where I was. I remembered Sister Alcantara's warning about getting between a hippo and the river – it would be dangerous to walk past them. I had only one option. I retreated back into the maternity unit and clambered out of a window at its rear. The detour I took back to the staff house (and my bed) was a mile and a half hike.

The morning arrived too quickly. As I yawned myself awake, I considered how different my life might be had I been a midwife in an English hospital. Through bleary eyes I noticed something black sticking out from under my pillow. Thinking it was the strap of my watch, I pulled it out, only to discover I was holding the tail of a snake. Instinctively, I grabbed hold of its head and tossed it out of the window. The whole incident was over in less than a second. As I sat on the edge of the bed my heart started to pound as if I'd been running. I felt hot, and then cold, as the chill of delayed shock crept over me. It was only a small snake but the majority of snakes in Uganda have a venomous bite. It was nothing short of a miracle that I hadn't been bitten. Not only did the creature spend the night inches away from my face, but it would have felt very threatened by my pulling it out from under my pillow by its tail. I could not have tucked in my mosquito net when I left for the emergency delivery. After meticulously checking I had tucked all the edges under this time, I had a wash and prepared for my shift in the operating theatre.

Jinja is the administrative centre for South Busoga district, under which Buluba fell. It is where the government officials are based and, of course, where we purchased everything we needed for our leprosy work that we didn't receive in donations. Jinja, in the Ugandan language, means 'a stone'. The town lies 3,750 feet above sea level and covers eleven square miles overlooking Lake Victoria, the Ripon Falls and the River Nile.

The Jinja stone (after which the town is named) is still in existence. It has an old fig tree growing next to it. The local people believed that there were powers associated with the stone and the tree and there is a history of sacrifices being made there. As late as 1951, the local

Conservancy Officer was approached to allow a chicken to be sacrificed on the stone. Permission was refused.

In July 1962 there was a wonderful week of celebrations to commemorate the centenary of Speke's discovery of the source of the Nile. I thought back to the moment I sat on the rock overlooking the Ripon Falls on my arrival to Buluba. So much had happened in the years that had passed since then. The festivities were held in the grounds surrounding the Speke Memorial that had been built on the west bank of the Nile. Several of Speke's descendants were present at the opening ceremony. On each day of the festival, there was a programme of special events and activities that took place in a huge field near to the memorial. All the children involved showed great discipline and precision as they performed traditional Asian dancing, Kisoga wrestling and an 1862 pageant. The magnificent band that accompanied the events was made up of children from the Uganda Foundation for the Blind.

Each night there was a military tattoo by the various army units and uniformed organisations: the Uganda Police Dogs Section, the Uganda Fire Service, and the King's African Rifles. On one of the evenings the 1st Battalion of the Gordon Highlanders gave a display of marching whilst playing their bagpipes and drums. It was disappointing that so many of the leprosy patients were unable to join in the celebrations at Jinja. Sister Alcantara must have had the same thought because she invited the Gordon Highlanders to visit the centre in Buluba. They agreed and delighted the patients with a wonderful display of marching and Scottish dancing in the compound. Later in the afternoon, the leprosy patients challenged the Highlanders to a game of football. The patients won the match – probably because they played in bare feet, while the soldiers were encumbered by their kilts and heavy army boots.

We were so glad that the Buluba leprosy patients were able to join in the centenary celebrations. After the soldiers had left, I heard the Battalion signature tune being played on what I thought were drums. I decided to investigate. On the far side of the compound were twelve small boys dressed in 'kilts' made from banana leaves, and beating empty four-gallon paraffin tins as their drums. They marched in a line, kilts swinging, their tune almost correct and their rhythm perfect. It was only sad the soldiers weren't still in Buluba to see them.

There are two rainy seasons in Uganda. They are described as the long rains (in April and May) and the short rains (during November). This was November.

There had been thunderstorms at Buluba earlier in the day, but the rain had petered out to a fine drizzle. Nevertheless, I was surprised to see the priest hurrying across the red sludge of the compound, his face creased against the rain. I opened the door to meet him.

'Oh, Sister, I was just coming to see you.'

'How can I help you, Father?' I said.

'I've been called to one of the villages. Apparently one of their houses has been struck by lightning and some people have been injured.'

I nodded. 'Just let me get my medical bag.' It was not unusual for the priest to ask me to accompany him when visiting a sick or injured person.

As we drew close to the village, we could hear no loud wailing so we knew no one had died. The houses in this particular village were circular and made of mud and wattle. Each had a large central wooden post that supported the grass roof and projected upwards from the centre of it, like the spike of an umbrella. The lightning had struck one of these poles, travelling down into the house and striking the men inside who had been

Chief giving Sister Ruth a present.

Land Rover in a forest.

Bajanjabbi at Nsambya.

Sister Ruth at a leprosy treatment centre giving out Christmas gifts.

A local witch doctor.

Villagers making water pots.

Owen Falls Dam.

Milking the cows – ample opportunity for watering down the milk.

Women dancing for their chief.

Sister Ruth and Sophie on the verandah at Buluba.

A canoe for Sigulu.

Unloading on Walumbe island from Sigulu.

Sister Ruth 'at home' on Sigulu.

Celebrations for new-born twins.

Children of leprosy patients.

Sister Ruth on holiday at the Klapprott's farm near Eldoret.

leaning against the post, talking together. We were shown inside and found four men sitting glumly on the floor. I examined them one by one. Their burns were unusual; the skin looked as though it had been peppered with hot cinders. Two of them had burns to their arms and legs, one to his back and the other to his face and scalp. I treated their injuries and, as the pain subsided and indignation at what had happened replaced the shock of the accident, they began to be more worried about the damage to their clothes.

'You can call at the mission for some new clothes as soon as you're feeling better,' Father assured them.

They seemed cheered at this thought, and the priest and I left them to the gentle teasing of their womenfolk.

Another occasion was far more serious. I was due to visit a leprosy centre in a village called Celelemuk. It was on a hill surrounded by huge outcrops of rocks, fifty miles from Buluba. The priest had arranged to say Mass there so, to save petrol, I travelled with him. As soon as we stepped out of the car, we were greeted by the patients, villagers and people from other villages who had gathered for Mass. It was a perfect day, with hot sunshine and a cloudless blue sky. The villagers were excited about the priest's visit and had planned a feast day once Mass was over. There were too many people to fit in any of their buildings so the service was going to take place outside. Herdsmen arrived accompanied by their cattle, goatherds with their goats; the villages' dogs and hens, used to being with company, followed on behind. Even the local witchdoctor had come dressed in his full regalia: a cloak made from barkcloth, with a necklace of shells, and feathers on his head.

Even before the priest was ready for Mass, drums began to beat and the women started to dance, many with their babies strapped to their backs. One of the ladies who wasn't dancing came forward to help us unload the truck. I handed her the suitcase containing the altar linen. The lady's friend came over to greet us. She stood between us, laughing and joking. She was no more than a few inches away from either of us when the lightning struck her. She crumpled to the ground. There were no other signs of a storm – no rain and no more lightning. Immediately, I knelt down beside her, and the priest joined me. Together, we tried to resuscitate her, but she had no pulse. As we knelt and prayed over her lifeless form, the news of what had happened surged like a wave around the village. The drums were silenced. The dancers stopped dancing and began to wail and shriek. The noise they made was difficult to bear. Father decided to take the lady's body to her village and provide whatever comfort he could to her family. Then he would report the matter to the police while I stayed behind, treating anyone who was sick, until he returned.

I sent one of the ladies to the local *dukka* to buy some tea and sugar so everyone could have some refreshment. To an outsider, it might have seemed insensitive to celebrate Mass after such an event, but many of the people had travelled more than fifteen miles to attend the service and they understood that it was the right thing to do. While I was talking to a young woman about her diet, the same lady who had helped with the suitcase rushed up to me.

'*Nnyabo*!' she cried. 'A terrible thing has happened!'

'What is it?' I wondered what could possibly have happened to rival the earlier incident.

'The goats, *Nnyabo*!'

She held up the beautifully embroidered fine Irish linen altar cloth. It was chewed and misshapen. The goats that had been milling around had discovered it hanging down from the altar and had thought it would make a good meal. Beautiful though it was, the cloth was not essential to the service and I told the lady not to worry. I was sure that the priest would understand. After I'd treated the last patient, I called everyone together and we talked about what had happened to the lady who had been killed. I then led prayers for her and for her family.

Later, when Father and I were returning to Buluba, we discovered that we had both remembered the same biblical story of the Lord's coming: of two people working together in a field; one is taken and the other spared.

The following week, I had a much more enjoyable surprise. A European family who had been based in Uganda were returning to England. While they were in Africa, they had acquired a dog: a short-haired, russet-coloured, miniature dachshund called Sophie. They hoped someone at Buluba would be willing to adopt her, as she couldn't go back with them to England. I gladly offered to take her. Soon, Sophie became my constant companion, following me around the compound and accompanying me on safaris to the various leprosy centres. The Ugandans had difficulty pronouncing 'ph' so she became known as 'Soapy'. As she travelled with me, it wasn't long before she was known throughout the district and was often greeted before I was. She was very gentle-natured and became a great favourite with the children.

It was around this time that I changed my name from Sister Aelred (the name I had been given by the Franciscan Missionary Sisters for Africa) to my 'real' name, and became known as Sister Ruth. The Vatican had decided that the names given to the Sisters at baptism were more important than their professed names and we were given the choice of reverting to our baptismal names. Some of my colleagues decided to remain with the name they had adopted but I was happy to be Ruth once more.

By the early 1960s there was already a small hospital at Buluba, with wards, a simple operating theatre and laboratory with basic facilities. Buluba was also the headquarters of the Leprosy Control System: all the planning, evaluation and statistical analysis of this organisation took place here. In 1965, the German Leprosy Relief Association donated a new 100-bed hospital that replaced the old facilities (though the old buildings were not demolished but converted into accommodation). This generous provision meant that Buluba was now equipped with a modern operating theatre, a more sophisticated laboratory and a physiotherapy unit (that also covered rehabilitation).

As part of our work to consolidate the Leprosy Control System, permanent centres were built in each of the eight counties in Busoga and were known as county units. Each unit comprised a house for the leprosy assistant, a clinic for outpatients, a small ward of eight beds, and accommodation for sixteen ambulant patients. The small ward made it possible to treat minor conditions such as slight or transient exacerbations of a patient's leprosy (more severe or acute reactions were serious and were treated at Buluba under Dr Blenska's supervision), anaemia, intestinal parasites, severe ulcers, or eye conditions not needing surgery. This meant that the patients did not have the inconvenience, or we the expense, of transport to Buluba and back. The accommodation for the ambulant patients was used for the short-term stay of patients who needed special care such as stabilisation of treatment or daily physiotherapy. The great advantage of these centres was that patients were not moved out of their own areas and remained in contact with their families and homes.

Once the eight county units had been established, the remaining non-permanent treatment villages were either closed or turned into aid posts. These aid posts, or peripheral units, were the underpinning of the Leprosy Control System. The original idea for these units was to shorten the distances patients had to travel for treatment, a long journey being one of the biggest deterrents to initial consultation and completion of treatment. As the Leprosy Control Officer, I visited these units regularly and examined new patients to confirm diagnosis and discuss treatment with the leprosy assistant. He would then arrange the day and time for his next visit to the unit to distribute treatment.

In areas where there was no general medical care, people who did not have leprosy would attend the county unit for non-leprosy medical care. This boded well for our hope of a successful integration of leprosy treatment into the general medical service in the future. I knew it was achievable; the leprosy work in Busoga had advanced dramatically since I started my post at Buluba many years before. Those of us (Sister Alcantara, Dr Blenska and I) who were involved with the future planning of leprosy control became aware that we needed more information about the local leprosy situation so that we could best shape the control system to fit the needs of the area. We consulted with Busoga's District Medical Officer, Dr Brian Wallace, and he gave his approval for us to attempt a case-finding survey of the district. Sister and I knew that we would need the cooperation of the chiefs and local people if the survey was to have any hope of success, and we approached various people accordingly.

The Chief Medical Officer for Uganda, Dr Kadama, a member of the Basoga tribe, expressed his interest in the survey, giving us plenty of encouragement and helpful advice. In addition, the invaluable practical help and interest we received from the *Saza* (senior chiefs) set an example for most of the lesser chiefs. Our eventual survey team was made up of *Saza, Gombolala* and *Muluka* local chiefs, two leprosy assistants, two clerks from local headquarters, a vaccination team, Dr Blenska and me – the Leprosy Control Officer.

Before the survey team began work, we gave lectures and informal talks to selective groups in the area. These included teachers, community development officers, police, local traders and, most importantly, the chiefs. We invited not only the *Saza* chiefs but also the *Muluka* chiefs. At these talks we distributed a booklet (that I had written with the help of a senior leprosy assistant) to those who could read. The question and answer style booklet was called *Kiki Ky' omanyi ku Bigenge*? or *What do you know about leprosy*? We made particular efforts to give it to as many teachers as possible so they could use it in their schools.

Each *Muluka* chief chose a location for the survey in his own area and the local people built simple grass enclosures for privacy during the examinations.

On the first day, many people came but no one offered to be examined. I suggested to the chief that he come forward to be examined, to show his people that there was nothing to fear. He agreed, and from then on it went smoothly. This approach proved useful on many subsequent occasions, with most of the chiefs prepared to set a good example.

Examinations were carried out on a family basis. It was hoped that basing our survey on the family unit would provide us with important epidemiological and ethnological data. If, during our examinations, the leprosy assistant or I found a person with suspected leprosy lesions, we referred the person to Dr Blenska for definitive diagnosis.

Dr Blenska liked to be able to take the specimens herself from any suspect nodules that might indicate lepromatous leprosy. She took the samples back to the lab at Buluba, where she would prepare microscope slides from the material taken from the lesions. The slides were stained with particular dyes to show up the presence of the leprosy bacteria. If bacteria were demonstrated on a skin smear, this was classified as a positive smear and indicated the multibacillary form of leprosy. The importance of distinguishing the various forms of leprosy lay in the different times for which treatment was required. Patients with a positive skin smear had to remain on drugs for much longer than those with negative smears. Neither could leprosy treatment be given on the basis of suspected disease. It was most important that a diagnosis of leprosy was not made hastily or lightly, because of the social and psychological consequences of such a diagnosis for both the patient and their family.

After the children had been examined for evidence of leprosy, they moved down the line to the vaccination team. Here, if they hadn't already received the immunisation course, they were given BCG (tuberculosis), polio and diphtheria vaccinations. Arrangements were made for them to attend for further immunisations at either their local medical centre or the nearest leprosy treatment centre. As a reward, and an incentive, each child was given a lollipop. On that first day of the survey, 416 lollipops were distributed before we gave up counting.

It was important to offer treatment as soon as possible to those found to have leprosy. So, immediately after we had finished examinations in a particular area we held a consultation with the *Muluka* chief. The details of all the new patients diagnosed during the examinations were then sent to the leprosy assistant in charge of the district centre nearest to where they lived. The assistant then took over responsibility for the treatment of these patients. We estimated that we examined more than four hundred and sixty-two thousand people during the survey. The percentage of new leprosy patients varied in different areas from 0.8 per cent to 4 per cent. Of this number, 1.2 per cent had positive skin smears. Another benefit of the survey was a number of absentee patients were discovered and re-started on treatment.

9.

Sigulu Island

After we'd completed the survey, I was talking to one of the chiefs about our success in Busoga; how many people we'd seen and been able to start on treatment. During the course of this conversation, a thought struck me.

'Are there any islands that are part of Busoga that I haven't visited?'

'There are some, but *Nnyabo,* you mustn't go to those.'

I pressed him for information and discovered that there were several islands in Lake Victoria that came under the jurisdiction of the Busoga Administration, none of which we had visited. The largest island was called Sigulu and had an estimated population of 2,000, mostly fishermen and their families. There were also smaller islands, two of which had approximately five hundred inhabitants. The islands lay in the 'restricted belt' – there were tsetse flies, which meant there was a danger of contracting the potentially fatal sleeping sickness. However, the chances of being bitten were slight because the grass and scrub that were the habitat of the fly were kept short by the local people and were sprayed regularly with insecticide by the health department.

'But *Ssebo,*' I insisted, 'we must visit these islands or the survey for Busoga will not be complete.'

'No. These people have never seen a white man before, or a white woman. It is not safe for you.'

'Well, we won't know unless we go.'

I left the chief, feeling frustrated, but as I thought about the potential danger of the islanders' reaction to me, a white woman, not to mention the risk of sleeping sickness, I tried to respect his decision. Over the next few weeks I would find my mind wandering to Sigulu and the other islands, imagining all the different reactions to my arrival. I prayed about the situation regularly. I finally came to the conclusion that I would talk it over with the District Medical Officer for Busoga, presenting the chief's concerns as well as my inclination, and then abide by his decision. I approached him, armed with the results of the survey for the rest of Busoga.

'I've recently discovered that there are some islands that haven't been covered as part of the survey. I'd very much like to visit them, but the *Saza* chief doesn't think that it's a good idea for me to go. What do you feel about it?'

After further discussion about the risks and the benefits, the District Medical Officer thought I ought to give it a go. The first problem that presented itself was transport, as the only approach to the island of Sigulu was by boat. The medical department owned a canoe with a small outboard motor that was used for tsetse fly control around the lake. The District Medical Officer offered to lend it to me together with an experienced boatman who knew the lake and its moods well. I was delighted.

A day was organised for me to look over the canoe and meet my skipper. Musa was a giant of a man: I was completely shadowed from the sun as he shook my hand in greeting. From this first meeting, I could tell he was both powerful and courteous. He was a member of the Jaluo tribe from northern Uganda. He was very familiar with

Lake Victoria because he accompanied the government officials when they were involved in tsetse control. Instantly, I felt sure I would be safe with him. He stepped sideways to reveal the canoe behind him, glaring red in the sunlight. It was made of wood and painted white inside. I was relieved to see that a white painted canopy had been erected towards the stern that would shelter me from Uganda's relentless sun. On the bow in bright white read BUSOGA MEDICAL DEPARTMENT.

I arranged a day for Musa to take me to Sigulu. He suggested we left in the morning because the lake would be calmer. I'd sent a message via an earlier boat to advise Sigulu's chief of the date of our visit, our estimated time of arrival, and of our requirements. Although Sophie accompanied me on my visits to the various leprosy centres, I felt that it was not appropriate to take her to Sigulu. Instead, I left her at Buluba, being looked after by the Sisters. I had no qualms about leaving Sophie in their care while I was away.

I decided to take Benedict with me to the island, as he was one of our most experienced senior leprosy assistants.

'Why are we taking so much soap, Sister?' Benedict asked on the day of departure as he carried a box full of soap tablets towards the canoe.

'Gifts, Benedict. We aren't taking any drugs this time. I just want to meet as many people as I can and do some examinations so I can assess what we might need to bring next time.'

He nodded and continued down towards the lake. The water in Thruston Bay looked so calm. I had to squint as the low morning sun playing across its surface dazzled me.

Benedict gave me his hand to help me into the canoe. 'Oh, Benedict, I'm looking forward to this!'

'Just wait until we're out of the bay and into the lake proper,' he smiled.

Musa had brought another young man with him as an assistant. I greeted him as Benedict handed Musa our food and flasks for the journey.

'What are those empty tin cans for?' I asked Musa, noticing the pile by my feet.

'Bailing out. The canoe sits low in the water, so when the lake is rough, the waves pour into the boat.'

'I see,' I said, trying not to sound alarmed. 'And the oars?'

'If the storm is too much for the outboard motor, we need to row. This is why I bring my assistant, and the oars.'

I tried to smile, hoping desperately that three men would be sufficient and I would not be called upon as a fourth oarsman!

The men pushed the canoe into the deeper water and jumped in. Musa lowered the outboard motor and we set off. As the crimson boat cut through the placid bay, I found it impossible to imagine the raging storms and torrents that Lake Victoria was notorious for. After fifteen minutes we emerged from the bay into the main lake. It was choppier, but not enough to cause any alarm. We chugged past a huge dark forest, fringed with a tiny beach. We could see crocodiles basking at the water's edge. I heard a peculiar noise and turned to see bubbles on the surface. As I continued to watch, water spurted up accompanied by a snorting sound.

'It is the hippos, *Nnyabo*. They are beneath the surface of the water, keeping out of sight,' Musa explained as he manoeuvred the boat out towards the middle of the lake. When I didn't reply, he continued. 'It's best to avoid them. I've heard of hippos coming up under a boat and tipping out the people in it. Then the crocs have an early lunch!'

Almost immediately I noticed a crocodile following the boat. It was huge. I'd never seen one so close before. I edged nearer to the front of the boat, not taking my eyes from our pursuer for a moment. The men didn't pay any attention to it, so I said nothing and, after a few minutes, I lost sight of it.

The only sound was the hum of the motor and a slight lapping of the water against the side of the canoe. Although the sun's intensity had increased there was a refreshing breeze on the lake and I felt so at peace, looking at the beautiful nature around me.

'Sister, look!' Benedict was pointing at a tree along the bank. It was unusual for him to betray such excitement. I followed his outstretched finger with my eyes. There, on a thick branch, perched a fish eagle. It was truly majestic: white head and neck, black wings with tawny plumage that gleamed in the sunlight. Had the bird not taken off in front of my eyes I shouldn't have believed it could fly, it was so enormous. As we watched, it crouched forward, then its vast black wings burst open, the feathers splayed out like fingers, and it soared high over our heads and out of sight. All that remained was the branch it had been sitting on, moving up and down. Even Musa looked impressed.

'We are almost here. I see Sigulu.'

We had been on the lake about an hour and a half. I had enjoyed my journey more than I could have anticipated, but as I made out the slight bump of the island breaking up the water in the distance, I became anxious to see Sigulu. As we drew nearer, I was surprised how big it appeared to be. There were figures on the beach and in the water; I realised they were either mending nets or washing clothes. It was a truly biblical picture – one I imagined Jesus must have come across many times during his life. It filled me with awe that I, too, was witnessing such a scene.

Musa steered us into land and Benedict helped me onto the beach. While the men pulled the boat onto the shore and unloaded, I wandered over to a group that were mending the nets. All of them were women. I spoke to one of the ladies in Lusoga, but she completely ignored me. Instead, I addressed one of the others, with the same result. I approached a third lady, who put down her net and turned to me. She put her thumb and first finger in her mouth and removed a cigarette. She spat and said, 'Aye.' Then she replaced the cigarette, closed her mouth over it and carried on with her mending, as if I wasn't there. I later discovered that women of this particular tribe always put the lighted end of a cigarette in their mouths and closed their lips over it. Later still I realised the women had been too frightened by this white stranger to make any sort of response to my greetings.

I turned to see a man on the beach. By his long trousers and shirt, I assumed he must be Sigulu's *Muluka* chief. Different tribes have different handshakes; I approached him with my hand outstretched, unsure how he would greet me. He took my right hand in his and shook it, then let go, shook it again and let go, then shook it a third time and placed his left hand on top.

'Welcome to my island, *Nnyabo*.'

'Thank you, *Ssebo*.'

'Please. You must call me Julius. Now come and meet my people. We have been waiting for you.'

I walked with Julius uphill, away from the lake, for about a mile. It was good to get out of the boat and move around, but the hill was so steep I was relieved when we reached a plateau and he slowed down. There were about a hundred people around us and, as we stopped, they began to clap. It was an eerie sound, so unlike the welcome I had received at the other leprosy centres where there were drums and singing and dancing. The clapping continued: a courteous acknowledgement of my arrival, coupled with the fear of seeing a white-skinned person for the first time. Once the clapping had ceased, I greeted them in their language and they answered me, which helped reduce the tension.

Julius showed me the enclosure that had been made out of grass for the privacy of the examinations. I confess I was relieved to retreat into it, feeling more confident meeting Sigulu's residents on a one-to-one basis. We wanted to examine islanders in family groups to be consistent with the survey we'd conducted for the rest of Busoga. Some islanders didn't want to be examined so we didn't pressurise them; from my previous experience of such situations, I knew if we waited they would soon find out there was nothing to fear, as the bush telegraph began to do its job.

We examined 1,859 adults, of which 184 had leprosy. Twenty had previously been treated in Uganda or Kenya. Every child under ten that we saw was covered in scabies, a highly contagious parasitic condition caused by a tiny mite that burrows into the skin and causes intense irritation. Some of the lesions were septic and suppurating; others were bleeding from being frantically scratched. Many of the children were anaemic and most had huge potbellies, suggestive of intestinal parasites or hookworm. Several of the women I saw were pregnant, but I thought it best not to do any antenatal examinations this time; instead, I just talked to them about their island and about fishing and mending nets.

No cows or goats were allowed on the island because it lay in the tsetse fly restricted area. As a result, there was a shortage of meat and milk in the inhabitants' diets. It was the custom that only the men and boys ate eggs, so the women ate virtually no protein. I had been on the island barely two hours and already I desperately wanted to do something to improve their diets and their health situation generally. On that first visit, I soon realised that a single day on Sigulu wouldn't be enough to care for all those who needed treatment, and to address the people's nutritional needs, let alone visit the smaller islands.

When we were ready to return to the mainland, Julius accompanied me down the hill to our boat.

'Julius, how do you get your supplies and medical care here?'

'People have to travel by boat either into Kenya or Uganda. It's a very expensive two-day journey, so people only go when they have to.'

'How do you think your people would respond if I were to visit again and stay on the island for a few days?'

He stopped walking, his face a picture of pure delight. Encouraged, I continued, 'It would mean I would have enough time to give medical care to the people on Sigulu, and visit the other islands.'

'Thank you, *Nnyabo*. That would be wonderful!'

'I can't promise anything now. I have to check with my superiors first.'

In fact, I had to give my report to the District Medical Officer and get his permission to start any new venture, especially as I would need both the canoe and Musa. I would also have to fit any further visits around my current leprosy control work across Busoga district, and my teaching of the student leprosy assistants at Buluba.

We were almost at the canoe when I caught sight of the most peculiar looking bird I'd ever seen, perched on the side of the boat.

'Look!' I said, pointing. 'What is that?'

Musa frowned. 'It's a bird, *Nnyabo*.'

'I know it's a bird! What *sort* of bird is it?'

'Hammerhead,' announced Benedict.

We drew nearer and it flew to another boat, from where it quietly watched us. It was dark brown with no distinctive markings whatsoever, just this strange truly hammer-shaped head. It clearly didn't impress my companions as it did me. They preferred the majesty of the fish eagle we had seen earlier.

As I was about to get into the boat, Julius presented me with a freshly caught fish, already gutted, and wrapped in a banana leaf. I thanked him; he had been crucial to the success of our visit. I hoped we would renew our acquaintance soon; I was already entertaining big plans for the advancement of health care on Sigulu Island. Musa started the motor and I watched the gentle *Muluka* chief and his islanders shrink into the horizon as our canoe ploughed back towards the mainland.

'Did you hear what I said to the chief, Benedict?'

'No, Sister.'

'I told him we'd like to come back to the island for a few days. I thought we would be able to help more people that way. What do you think?'

'I think you are right, Sister.' He was looking out at the water as he spoke. After a pause, he turned back to me. 'But where would we sleep? And what would we do for food?'

'Let's think about all of that another time,' I yawned. 'I'm too tired now.'

'But Sister, we haven't eaten. Shall I put out the sandwiches and tea?'

'Oh yes, Benedict. That would be lovely.'

We savoured the welcome refreshment and the next thing I knew, I was waking up in Thruston Bay, just in front of Buluba Leprosy Centre. It had been a ten-hour day, but I had a much better idea about what I could do when I next visited Sigulu. I said goodbye to Musa and his helper and gave them the fish and a bar of soap each, by way of a thank you.

When I gave my report to the District Medical Officer, he agreed for me to visit Sigulu monthly, holding leprosy and general medical clinics. He also said I could visit the other islands provided the local chief knew beforehand and was willing to provide any necessary protection. Fear is a very powerful emotion and although I didn't feel I looked very threatening, white people hadn't been to some of the islands before. The District Medical Officer was right to be wary of the people's reaction to me. I had been fortunate that Sigulu had such a good chief in Julius: chiefs of the other islands might not be so accommodating.

I was delighted with the outcome of the meeting. Not only was I allowed to revisit Sigulu and the other islands, but also UNICEF would supply the leprosy drugs and soap. Additionally, the District Medical Officer agreed to supply the drugs and equipment I would need for the general medical work, together with Musa and the use of the canoe.

Dr Blenska shared my enthusiasm and hoped to accompany me when the time came to spend the night on Sigulu. However, she did suggest that it might be a good idea to make several more day visits to Sigulu so that the people would get used to us, then when we made overnight visits they would be happier. I couldn't wait.

10.

Eggs, Fish and Banana Leaves

I watched with trepidation as Musa loaded the last of our luggage into the canoe. It was to be our second visit to Sigulu and this time we were taking leprosy medication and other drugs, dressings and equipment including basins and towels for the medical staff. Seeing it all lying in the canoe made me glad our vessel was built to hold eight. We were only going for the day so we planned to arrive at Sigulu at 9.30 a.m., which meant leaving Thruston Bay at 7.30 a.m. As on our first visit, the lake was fairly calm. As the boat approached the island, I was relieved to see Julius on the beach ready to meet us with a group of men who could carry all the equipment up the steep hill.

Only eighty people came for help that day, ten of whom were suffering from leprosy. As we were not overwhelmed with patients, I was able not only to examine several pregnant ladies, but also to have enough time to talk to them and get to know them a little. When Benedict and I stopped to have our sandwiches and coffee, the schoolchildren entertained us with singing and dancing. Julius was always available to help us if we needed anything. With his now familiar smile, he took the opportunity to introduce me to two of his wives and their children. I learned that there were others but they were mending nets so I would meet them on my next visit.

I treated the last of the patients while Benedict began to take some of the equipment back down to the beach. I was relieved not to have been welcomed by the eerie applause this time. As I collected the last of my things, I realised I was not nearly as exhausted as I had been on the previous visit to Sigulu – physically or emotionally.

As Julius walked with me down the hill to the canoe, I could see Musa scurrying about and looking up at the sky.

'What's the matter, Musa?' I called.

He pointed to the lake. 'A storm is coming. We must hurry.'

I noticed the little red boat was dipping up and down much more than I had seen before.

'We are carrying a lot of weight, *Nnyabo*,' Musa frowned.

'We will be all right though, Musa?'

'Yes, *Nnyabo*,' he said as Benedict helped me aboard.

The canoe's progress was slower through the rough lake, but I kept looking at Musa, and his strong warrior face showed no trace of anxiety. I bowed my head against the rain that had started to fall, hoping it wouldn't be long until I was back at the staff house at Buluba drinking some tea.

Sigulu was out of sight when the storm struck. Rather than ride the waves, the canoe seemed to sit in a trough with great walls of water on either side. Every few seconds a wave would crash over the side drenching us even more than the driving rain. Thunder roared around us and lightning seared the sky above. There was water everywhere, even round my ankles. Benedict and I reached for a can each and began to bail. Musa struggled against the wind to keep us on course. I tried to pray but couldn't. I kept thinking of the gospel story of Jesus calming the storm and I hoped desperately he would do the same for me. I couldn't concentrate on anything for too long other than bailing out the canoe and trying not to swallow too much water. Oddly, one of my main concerns was that I shouldn't do anything to let myself down in front of the boys!

As we wrestled into Thruston Bay, the wind changed direction, and the water, although still rough, no longer poured into the boat. We continued to bail. Gradually the water around our ankles receded enough for us to put down our cans.

'Are you OK, Sister?'

'Yes, thank you, Benedict.'

He sat down next to me while Musa guided us into land. Silently I thanked God that we had arrived safely. The journey from Sigulu that should have taken two hours had taken six.

As I lay in bed that night savouring the soft sheets, the stillness of the bed beneath me, I hoped that I would never have to face a storm like that again. I thought about the red canoe that had taken such a pounding. The Africans who made these vessels were wonderful craftsmen. If we had been in any other type of boat, I doubt we would have survived.

During our fourth day-visit to the island, I told Julius that when I came to the island the following month, I would stay for three days. Clearly delighted, he informed me that there would be an empty teacher's house available for the men to sleep in – they would only need to bring sleeping bags and blankets. Once back on the mainland, I bought a tent, camp beds, cooking equipment and hurricane lamps and torches (as there was no electricity on Sigulu). As I planned the three days, I realised how precious our time would be, especially on the days we were due to travel to the other islands. With this in mind, I enlisted the help of Ludovico. He was a young man who had been treated for leprosy and felt indebted to us for curing him. Although, at first, he'd been cast out by his family, he'd been accepted again once he was cured. However, he'd been away from home, at Buluba, for so long that he was happier to stay with us, returning to visit his family every now and then. Unfortunately, he hadn't the education to be trained as a leprosy assistant, but he would do odd jobs for me in my office. I had the district stores here; he would dust them and keep them in order for me. He oversaw the feeding of the budgies and would feed Sophie when I was going to chapel to say prayers with the rest of the community. He was an ideal addition to our team, to carry water and run errands. He could also remain on Sigulu to watch our belongings while we visited the other islands. The only thing I needed to teach him was cooking. He learned quickly how to make tea, but the only meal he was able to master was fish and chips. I knew there would be no shortage of fish on the island so we wouldn't go hungry. Ludovico was more than happy to help.

Dr Blenska was unable to come to Sigulu on this first overnight visit so she kindly agreed to look after Sophie for me. For safety and propriety, it seemed appropriate that I take a female companion for the overnight trip. One of Buluba's Sisters, Sister Felicity, was in her eighties. A week before my proposed visit to the island, her niece came to visit her. As Sister Felicity was unable to show Ruth, her niece, much of the country, she asked if I could take her on some of my routine visits to the county units and aid posts across Busoga. We got on very well on these trips so I invited Ruth to accompany me to Sigulu.

Musa had advised me that it would be better to leave from Lugala, a port fifty miles away from Buluba. We would be carrying a lot more equipment than before, not only extra supplies for three days, but the tent and extra cans of petrol so that we could travel to the other islands. At Lugala, Musa could load the canoe directly from the Land Rover, and our vehicle could be left securely in the compound of the *Muluka* chief during our absence. The other advantage of leaving from Lugala was a shorter journey across Lake Victoria. This was important, as the increased weight in the canoe would make our progress much slower.

One disadvantage of Musa's plan was that it meant we had to leave Buluba before dawn. We had loaded the Land Rover the previous evening, and there was only just enough space in the back for Ludovico to wedge himself amongst the tent poles and medical supplies. Ruth sat in the passenger seat and I drove with Benedict perched between us. The rattle of the engine as I turned the ignition key broke into the silence of that strange time of quiet between the end of the night and the beginning of a new day. It was the time of year when the stars seem at their largest. The Southern Cross, the most important constellation in the southern hemisphere, was particularly bright and beautiful; the Plough hung in the sky upside down to how I'd been taught to recognise it by my father, all those years ago at home in England.

The journey to Lugala took us through a forest. The trees either side of us were so tall, the tops disappeared out of sight. We could no longer see the stars. Beautiful mahoganies merged into the inky sky, their branches festooned with orchids and ferns. We couldn't see the flowers but their perfume mingled with the musk of the trees, and the smell of warm damp earth permeated everything. We passed a procession of monkeys, the headlamps of the Land Rover picking out the two young ones in front, followed by the mother holding the hand of another youngster, with a baby on her back. The large male of the family followed behind. They stopped briefly to watch us pass, without fear it seemed.

I had been driving for more than an hour and felt tired owing to our early start; I saw the snake just in time.

I pushed down on the brakes hard, sending a box of soap careering into Ludovico. Lying across the middle of the road was an enormous python. The Land Rover stopped within a few feet of the snake. It didn't move and, initially, neither did we.

'What is it, *Nnyabo*? Why have we stopped?' Ludovico contorted his neck to get a view of the road. 'Oh!' he said. 'What shall we do, *Nnyabo*? Benedict? Can we drive over it?'

'No, Ludovico, it's too big.' I answered. 'What do you think, Benedict?'

'I think, Sister, that it has just eaten – see the hump in its middle? It will be sluggish from its meal so I think we should try to drive round it.'

Ruth and I must have looked alarmed, because he then offered to get out and direct the manoeuvring.

'No, Benedict, it's dark; it's not safe for you to get out. I'll try to drive round it.'

I crept forward, narrowly skirting the python, but scraping the side of the Land Rover against a tree. As we continued, I hoped our journey would not hold any more adventures.

Further on, there were some openings in the forest where we could make out little round mud-walled, grass-roofed huts. Of course, there was no one around, so we were unable to discover why they were living in the dense forest.

Gradually the trees thinned and the road narrowed. Twice Benedict and Ruth banged heads as the Land Rover hit a bump. After seven miles on this road, the lake appeared.

Lugala Port was not a port in the strictest sense, but merely a place for local fishermen to land their catches and take them to the market. Musa was already busy, preparing the canoe for the journey, and he soon unloaded the Land Rover and transferred everything we needed into the canoe. Benedict gave the keys of the Land Rover to an *askari*.[1] The officer had been primed and was waiting to take the vehicle to the compound of the *Muluka* chief where we hoped it would be safe until our return.

Once this was done, we piled into the boat and set off for our first long-stay visit to Sigulu Island. The lake was almost motionless. There was a beautiful yet deceptive dreamlike quality about the African dawn. Though heavily laden, the small canoe ploughed through the water, churning a wake of silver spray. There was an ethereal quality in the light as the first faint pink and lavender hues tinged the sky and were reflected in the lake's surface. It was a perfect time for quiet meditation. I knew that the sunrise would bring stark heat and naked reality in the form of sickness and disease.

Julius stood on the shore, smiling, his arms outstretched as we clambered out of the boat. Now he knew me, he always greeted me with his arms open. Once I was within touching distance he lowered his arms and shook my hand in the greeting of his tribe. He had gathered several men to carry everything from the canoe up the hill to where we would be working. A huge crowd was waiting for us as we reached the summit; we realised it was going to be a long day. Benedict and I left our belongings with Ruth and Ludovico for the time being and immediately set about getting ready to treat patients.

My first job was to choose a suitable location to set up the dispensary. On the hill's plateau was a huge old mango tree with massive wide, shady branches; it was an ideal place, on flat ground and with protection from the scorching sun.

'Julius, are there any tables and chairs we could use?' I asked.

'Yes, *Nnyabo*! Wait here while I send someone to fetch them. It will take about twenty minutes.'

While we were waiting for the furniture to arrive, we decided it would be a good time to have a sandwich and some coffee so we wouldn't need to break once we'd started the examinations. While we were eating, the men arrived with the furniture. I pointed to the mango tree and asked them to set it down.

'No, *Nnyabo*.'

'No? Why not?'

'It's a bad tree.'

'What do you mean, it's a bad tree?'

But they wouldn't say anything else. There was no other tree nearby and we certainly couldn't work out in the blazing sun all day. I walked around the tree with Benedict. Neither of us could find anything wrong with it, so we decided to set up the dispensary regardless. As we did so, the muttering of the crowd grew and grew. It was reminiscent of the eerie clapping that greeted me on my first visit to the island. I sent Benedict among the people to try to ascertain what the problem was. He emerged from the crowd looking concerned.

'The people are afraid, Sister. They think the tree is bad because there is a devil in it. They told me that people put sacrifices there at certain times.'

'What should we do, Benedict? Look at all these people who've come. We won't be able to help half of them if we don't start soon.'

'Maybe we should send for the chief and ask him to talk to the people.'

That seemed a sensible suggestion so we sent Musa to find him. Julius arrived without delay. He listened to what his people were saying, and then spoke to them, gently explaining why we had to work under the tree.

'None of you needs to stay if you do not want to be treated. Each of you can choose for yourselves.'

He then came to where we were standing under the tree and began looking at the different drugs and equipment we had laid out. The crowd was hushed. After about ten minutes, a lady came forward with two small children. We examined them all, and gave them their treatment and a piece of soap. They left us, smiling.

Others followed in dribs and drabs. After about an hour, there were more than a hundred islanders queuing for treatment. Laughing and talking had replaced the sinister muttering of earlier. When we had finally seen and treated the last patient, Ludovico produced tea and bananas and we talked over the day's many events. Despite the various hiccups, it had been successful overall and augured well for the future. I personally had learned an important lesson in diplomacy. I was reminded again how fortunate the people of Sigulu were, to have such a wise and understanding chief. If it had not been for Julius, the whole day could have been a fiasco.

We decided that the best site for my tent was near the infamous mango tree, much to the consternation of many of the islanders. While Benedict and Ludovico put it up for me, children, followed by the more curious adults, flocked round. They had never seen a tent before and were amazed at what it looked like once the canvas was properly erected. Some of the people raced off to bring their relatives to look at it. I overheard comments such as 'This is Sister's house and she is going to live here while she is staying with us' and 'Is she going to sleep on the floor?'. Once Benedict and Ludovico had finished, I let the bystanders have a look inside. There were two camp beds, a little stool and a table. The men were sleeping in a two-roomed teacher's house. They were going to use one of the rooms as a dormitory and the other had a table and chairs where they could eat. We were also able to use the school kitchen for our cooking.

The next morning we loaded the canoe with drugs and soap. Julius decided to come with us to introduce us to the people living on one of the islands. En route, he instructed Musa to pull alongside one of the fishing boats. Julius then told one of the fishermen that he wanted a fish for Sister. The fisherman handed Julius a beautiful tilapia; it was still jumping as he lowered it into the boat.

'Let me give you some money for the fish,' I said to Julius and the fisherman.

'No, *Nnyabo*. That is not necessary,' Julius replied as he gestured to Musa to continue. When I pressed him to explain, he pointed to the numbers on the bows of the fishing boats.

'They all have to register each year. I allow some off registering providing they give me fish when I want some. The man who gave you the fish is one of those.'

As we approached the island, Musa had to manoeuvre the boat up a very narrow creek between large rocks, avoiding the overhanging papyrus. I had full faith in our skipper and was feeling more concerned about the reaction we might receive. I needn't have worried; most of the people on this island had been to Sigulu on the day of the leprosy survey and seemed quite relaxed as we got out of the canoe. Julius gave my fish to one of the women on the beach and asked her to gut it, wash it and wrap it in banana leaves to keep it cool until my departure.

We unloaded the boat and went up to the compound of the chief of the island. As we set up our little dispensary, people began to dance. It probably seems bizarre to westerners, but in Africa it is indicative of celebration or pleasure – it is the custom to dance at weddings, at the birth of twins, when chiefs or other people visit, and for the sheer joy of dancing. I took it as acceptance of my presence on their island.

I knew from the records of the survey that there were only two people on the island with leprosy, but more than fifty came forward for general medical treatment. I was able to examine and talk to ten pregnant women about their diet and health. As well as treating many of the children for scabies, we also saw several children presenting symptoms of severe malnutrition. I explained to the parents of each child how important it was to try to improve their diet. With the help of the District Medical Officer, I had managed to obtain supplies of powered milk from UNICEF. I could now regularly distribute several packets each to the women and children. At first, Benedict had to demonstrate how to mix the powder with water for drinking. Initially, the women were reluctant to taste the reconstituted milk but after Benedict and I drank it and showed that it was safe, they started to sample it; it was entertaining to hear their tasting comments.

During our journey back to Sigulu, I chatted to Julius.

'Now I'm staying on the island, I'll have spare time in the evening. I was wondering whether, after supper and after I've said my prayers, I might talk to some of the women about diet.'

Julius nodded encouragement.

'I could ask if they would like me to teach them some reading and simple sewing, too; the moon's so bright.'

'Yes, *Nnyabo*. That would be wonderful. You know, if you conquer the women, you have conquered the island.'

Ludovico had been watching out for us. I think he must have known I had been given a fish because, as he met the boat, he greeted me with: 'Fish and chips, *Nnyabo*?'

'Yes please, Ludovico.'

I handed him the tilapia and by the time we'd unloaded the boat and I'd had a wash, the fish and chip supper was ready. With the meal, Ludovico provided some tea. It was slightly bluish and I only had a sip. I was glad I'd been cautious: it was vile.

'Ludovico! Where did you get the water for the tea?'

'From the lake.'

'From the edge of the lake?'

'Yes, *Nnyabo*.'

'From the edge of the lake where the people bathe and wash their clothes?'

'Yes, *Nnyabo*.'

I tipped the tea onto the ground. After the long day in the sun, I had been so looking forward to a nice cup of tea. Benedict rescued me.

'Next time you go to get water, Ludovico, you could go in our boat and row out into the lake, then you can fill the container with much cleaner water.'

I nodded my agreement.

'Yes, Benedict. Yes, *Nnyabo*,' Ludovico said.

On subsequent overnight stays, we chose the days of the month when there would be a full moon: it was so bright we could do our chores and even read by its light. I always had a female companion on these trips, and often it was Dr Blenska.

One day before a treatment session, I gave one of the men some tablets to take with a drink of water. Before popping them into his mouth, he put his hands together and recited the whole of the Lord's Prayer.

'Are you a Christian?' I asked him.

'No, *Nnyabo*.'

'Where did you learn that prayer?'

'At the beer pots.'

I smiled to myself – what a wonderful way to evangelise! It was very likely that one of the children, who would have been taught the prayer at school, had gone home and taught it to their parents. In turn, the prayer had been passed on at the beer pots.

At night it was the custom for Sigulu's men to congregate on their little wooden stools around vast clay pots. These pots held gallons of very potent home-brewed beer. Each man had his own straw, called a *lusekki*, made from a local plant. The straws were two feet long and beautifully decorated by the women with tiny coloured beads that they knitted together; yellow, blue, green and red; each one a different pattern. At the end of the straw was a very fine filter to prevent the drinker slurping a mouthful of grain. Unfortunately, drinking through a straw meant that the men rarely knew how much they had consumed and gradually became more and more drunk. Often after we had gone to our tent to sleep, my companion and I found ourselves woken by the sound of raucous shouting and even the sound of beer-induced skirmishes. On one such night, I was woken by an urgent whisper.

'Sister! Sister!'

It sounded like Benedict.

'Sister! Please come.'

I poked my head out of the tent. Benedict and Ludovico stood wide-eyed in front of me. Ludovico was shifting from foot to foot, while Benedict explained, 'There has been a fight, Sister. One of the men is hurt. I think it's bad. Can you come?'

I pulled on my coat and my boots and the man was soon brought to me, held up by several of the drinkers. His hands were covering his face, and blood dripped through his fingers, spattering onto the sand. We sat him on a chair outside my tent and prized his hands from his face. Despite the moonlight it was difficult to see his injury until Ludovico lit the hurricane lamp. He had a large gash across his forehead and the skin at the lower edge of the wound was flapping away from his skull, as if he'd been scalped. It would never stop bleeding, or heal, without stitches. Although I had brought sterile dressings and cotton wool to Sigulu, I hadn't brought any suturing materials. The journey to Kenya or Uganda to a hospital would take more than three hours and the man was bleeding profusely. The only solution I could think of was to use my ordinary needle and thread to sew up the wound.

Ludovico quickly lit the primus stove so we could boil the cotton and sewing needle. I had no anaesthetic, but our patient was so drunk he didn't flinch once as I put more than twenty stitches in his forehead. Benedict took him back to the schoolhouse for the night and the next morning he was fit enough to go back to the village. When he returned to have his stitches removed I was relieved to see how well his wound had healed, despite the unorthodox repair technique. He handed me a bunch of bananas and a basket of eggs by way of a thank you. He was rather more coherent this time than when I'd first met him. We shared the bananas and I gave the eggs to the boys, but didn't enquire how many were edible.

On our overnight stays, after we'd eaten our evening meal, my companion and I would take advantage of the full moon's brightness and the absence of the menfolk at their nightly drinking sessions to visit the women in their homes. They would sit outside chatting with us. I remember on one occasion I was talking to a group of women about the gospels and we had got on to Mary, the mother of Jesus.

'Has anybody got any questions?' I asked.

'Yes, *Nnyabo*.'

'What is it?'

'Was Mary black or white?'

I paused. 'Well, she wasn't black and she wasn't white.'

'Oh, she was an Indian, then,' one of the other women stated knowingly.

'No,' I replied. 'She wasn't an Indian.'

'Well, what was she, then?' They wanted to know.

'Well, she was a Jew.'

They looked blank.

'Oh,' one said slowly – and that was the end of the conversation.

11.

The Bishop Visits Sigulu

About two years after my first visit, we received enough money from the German Leprosy Relief Association to build a small permanent clinic on Sigulu. It was the first permanent building, made of brick and wood, on the island. It included a ward of five beds and a labour room. This was done in the hope that eventually it would be possible to have a midwife and leprosy assistant living on Sigulu permanently.

Once the building was finished, I suggested we invite an important person to open it officially. Julius called a meeting to ask who the people would like to perform this ceremony and then reported back to me.

'They have decided that the bishop is suitably important. There are also some couples that wish to get married and some parents who want to have their children baptised. Do you think the bishop would be able to do all this?'

'What a lovely idea! I'll speak to him, Julius. I'll let you know next time I visit Sigulu.'

Most of the couples that wanted to be married had been living as man and wife for many years (in two cases, for more than twenty years) and the majority had several children. I was unsure how the bishop would feel about this. When I returned to the mainland I went to see him. Bishop Grieff was Dutch but spoke the Ugandan language – and English – fluently. He agreed to open the building and speak to the couples wishing to be married, and the parents of those children who were to be baptised. He put the date in his diary and agreed to sleep on the island, which would be necessary if he was to have enough time to perform the various ceremonies.

On the appointed day, I was relieved that Bishop Grieff had decided to keep things simple and left all his ceremonial paraphernalia at home. He was carrying his crozier, his staff of office, but wore the ordinary vestments of any priest celebrating Mass. As the canoe approached, the crowds of people waiting on the beach broke into singing and dancing. Many had come from the outlying islands to see him. The singing paused while Julius made a speech of welcome and then erupted again as the bishop was escorted from the shore. Flowers had been strewn along the path up the hill, bunting made from strips of material hung from the trees, and the aroma of roasting goat meat wafted down to us. I was very honoured to be asked to eat with the bishop and the invited chiefs, as it was normal for the women only to serve the men, not to join them for the meal.

The schoolchildren entertained us while we ate, laughing as they sang and danced around us. It was often difficult to break up these gatherings, but I knew the bishop wanted to see various people before darkness fell. He announced to the people, in their language, a time for Mass the following day, then stood up to leave.

I had been worried about where the bishop could sleep, but Benedict had come up with the great idea of using the new labour ward as a bedroom for him. Everything in there was clean and fresh, not yet having been used. There was a washbasin and stand and, most importantly, a door that closed so Bishop Grieff could have some quiet when he wanted. Ludovico was assigned to be his butler – making tea and sandwiches for supper and fetching water for washing.

Soon after the bishop had left for his quarters, Benedict and I went to see some sick people who had arrived, during the meal, for treatment. Eventually, I was able to retire to my tent, lulled to sleep by the sound of the drums and *dongo*[1] playing for the feast.

After Mass the next morning, Bishop Grieff told me he would marry ten couples and baptise twenty-two children at a ceremony starting at 10.30 a.m. This left us very little time to decorate the mud-walled schoolroom, which was functioning as a temporary chapel. Although the building was rather crude for a chapel, its tin roof glinted brilliantly in the morning sun, and inside, bunting had been hung from the walls and greenery strewn round the edges. While Musa and one of the schoolchildren went to collect the happy couples and children for baptism, the headmaster and Ludovico made an altar rail out of banana tree trunks. Once they had finished, I prepared the altar for Mass and Benedict escorted Bishop Grieff and the holy baptismal oil.

The baptisms took place first. The children were dressed smartly in their school uniforms and only a few shed tears as the holy water splashed on their foreheads. Once all twenty-two had been baptised, the couples to be married were invited to come forward and kneel along the length of the banana tree altar rail. The bishop had visited them on the previous evening so they knew what to say. All went perfectly until the bishop reached the sixth couple. As he had done with the previous five couples, he asked the lady if she would take the man next to her to be her husband.

'No,' she replied.

The bishop looked surprised. '*Nnyabo*, will you take the man next to you to be your husband?'

'No,' she said, slightly louder.

He inhaled, perplexed, and then coaxed, 'Will you take *this man*' – he patted the man next to her on the shoulder – 'to be your husband?'

'No!'

There was silence in the schoolroom. Bishop Grieff leaned towards her, 'But yesterday you told me that you wanted to marry the man you have been living with.'

'Yes, *Ssebo*. But he's not my man. Mine's down there!' and she pointed further down the line. I stifled a chuckle at the serious mismatch that had narrowly been averted. The dialogue in the local language with its particular intonations and exclamations seemed to make it more entertaining. The two men who were out of line rearranged themselves, so that when the bishop asked the lady the question a fourth time, she said, 'Yes!' The remaining couples were all married uneventfully.

Sadly we couldn't stay for long after lunch to enjoy the celebrations as Bishop Grieff had other appointments on the mainland. Julius and the other chiefs escorted us to the boat and presented the bishop with his gift of two fish and several eggs, cleaned and wrapped in banana leaves. I only hoped they would be edible. We had a calm journey across the lake and Bishop Grieff remarked how interesting and encouraging he had found the visit. The rest of us just smiled, relieved that everything had passed off without disaster.

Over the course of the next few months, we continued with our overnight visits to the islands. On one occasion, Dr Blenska and I visited a tiny island known as Bird Island that was inhabited by only about seventy-five people. We hadn't been there long before we discovered the reason for its name – massive eagles stared down at us from the treetops, blinking and ruffling their feathers.

'Sister! Watch out!'

I was aware of a flapping above me and a shadow covering the ground where I stood. Through my thin veil, I felt a sharp crack on the top of my head. I winced.

'Are you hurt, Sister?' Dr Blenska's usually smiling face looked alarmed.

'I don't think so,' I replied as my hand strayed to the place where the eagle had pecked me. 'Just a bruise, I expect.'

Before ten minutes passed two more eagles descended, giving both of us pecks on our heads. There was no permanent building on the island for us to use as cover from the eagles and we wondered together what to do. Fortunately, Dr Blenska had an ingenious idea. The equipment we had brought from Sigulu included our enamel washbasins – one for personal use, and one for medical work. These we inverted and placed over our heads. The heavy basins weren't very comfortable, and I expect we looked ridiculous, but it was certainly preferable to the pecks!

The people on Bird Island were very poor. Their main diet was small fish that resembled sardines. These they hung to dry on the trees and then smoked them. When it was time to eat, the chief presented Dr Blenska and me with several of the fish. We always ate what we were given as to refuse would have been a discourtesy to our hosts. The fish were not unpleasant, but they were very strong and tasted of smoke.

The chief of the island had instructed that a shelter be built for the privacy of our examinations. There were limited materials available so the islanders had hung up some of their sleeping mats for the purpose. It worked well and we were able to examine and treat all those who came to us. Once we had finished for the day we felt hot and dusty, so I asked the village headman to leave the shelter up until we had had a wash. I placed my enamel washbasin – my earlier protection from the eagles – on its wooden tripod and washed myself while Dr Blenska wrote up some of the day's records. Once I was clean and dry, I went to find her. She wanted to finish what she was doing so about half an hour elapsed between my leaving the shelter and her going for her wash. There was still enough light to read so, while I was on my own, I settled down with my notes.

'Where is it?'

I looked up from my papers into Dr Blenska's puzzled face. 'Where is what?'

'The shelter – the basin. It's gone!'

'Gone?'

'Gone,' she affirmed.

I went back with her to the spot where the shelter had been. There was nothing there. Some of the islanders must have been watching for us to finish, so when Dr Blenska didn't follow me straight away, they had assumed that we no longer needed the shelter, and had come to retrieve their sleeping mats.

We made our way back to our tent where we would be spending the night, only to discover that the washbasin and tripod had been left outside. By this time it was nearly dark. Dr Blenska decided to wash inside the tent, but as soon as she lit the hurricane lamp, her silhouette was clearly illuminated through the canvas. She managed to preserve her modesty with me holding the lantern to the outside of the tent so that she had enough light to wash by, but her form was not displayed to the rest of the island!

During our next overnight visit to Sigulu, Dr Blenska and I visited another island. It was January, the middle of the hot dry season. Ludovico had remained on Sigulu so only Benedict and Musa were able to help us carry our equipment to where we were to set up our temporary clinic. We were able to stay on this island overnight, so while Benedict and Musa put up our tent, Dr Blenska and I prepared a dispensary. There were no chairs other than the little drinking stools so we had to conduct all our examinations standing up. There was also very little shade. I was relieved I was no longer impeded by a full-length habit and instead wore a shorter doctor's coat and light veil.

By the time we were ready to see the first patients, a huge queue had formed. There were so many people to see, we didn't have time to pause for lunch.

When, eventually, we were able to have supper, I could taste the dust in the roof of my mouth. We deci-ded that we needed to have some sort of a bath before we went to bed so we arranged for our tent to be moved down to the water's edge. Under cover of darkness, we took turns to go into the lake. There was always a danger of crocodiles so while Dr Blenska was in the water, I shone the beam of our powerful torch around her. I scanned for the red eyes of any lurking crocodiles, ready to shout a warning at the first signs of anything suspicious, so she knew to get out. After she emerged and dried herself, Dr Blenska held the torch for me. It was the quickest bath I've ever had! That night I struggled to sleep, imagining every noise I heard was the sound of hungry crocodiles slinking out of the lake and surrounding the tent. As soon as it was morning, we petitioned Benedict and Musa to move the tent back to its original site, under a tree.

As I was giving my regular report to the District Medical Officer, he told me he would like to visit Sigulu himself and see how the work was progressing. Instead of the canoe, he decided to use the large Ugandan government cruiser that was used by government officials and dignitaries. When I got out of the car at the port of Jinja, I almost didn't recognise our skipper. Musa was dressed in a spotless white uniform, with Uganda's traditional red, gold and black stripes on his epaulettes, complete with peaked white cap bearing the Uganda emblem. At the side of the boat hung a rope ladder. I looked down at my calf-length white coat.

'How am I supposed to get aboard?' I called to the District Medical Officer, who was already on the deck.

'Musa? Help Sister aboard,' he called.

Immediately I felt myself being lifted over Musa's shoulder, like a sack of potatoes. He climbed halfway up the rope ladder, and dumped me on the deck. He went back down the ladder, stood to attention and saluted the District Medical Officer.

'Sister, Sir!'

Once Benedict, Musa and the drugs and equipment were aboard, we set off. It took only three-quarters of an hour to get to Sigulu in the cruiser. Julius was there to greet us, together with a crowd of islanders. We walked to the infamous mango tree that had originally caused the islanders so much consternation, and set up the dispensary as usual. While we treated patients, the headmaster took the District Medical Officer to the school where he introduced him to the pupils and acted as interpreter. As we left, Julius presented him with the usual gift of eggs and fish.

'What were your impressions of the day?' I asked the District Medical Officer on the return journey.

'It is good.'

'There's a permanent building for my clinic once a month but no medically trained staff living on the island. Do you think there may be a possibility of having a permanent leprosy or medical assistant on Sigulu?'

'I do not think so, no, Sister. There isn't enough work for that. But I'd like you to carry on with what you're already doing.'

As the men began to unload the cruiser, I became concerned about how to disembark. Benedict climbed onto the rope ladder first and Musa helped me over the side and onto the ladder. From there I managed to climb down myself, keeping my dignity reasonably intact.

The following day, Benedict and I were returning from a visit to a leprosy county unit, when Benedict advised me that there was trouble close to one of the roads we would be using.

'What sort of trouble?' I asked.

'The Baganda and the Basoga.'

I raised my eyebrows. It wasn't uncommon for a dispute between two people to lead to a dispute between two tribes.

'I think I know another way,' I suggested. 'It's narrow and potholed but I think the Land Rover should manage it.'

'Yes, Sister, I think we should try it.'

We followed the route for a few miles until we met with a roadblock of branches and tree trunks. On top of them stood a man with his arms akimbo, holding a *panga*.[2]

I wound down the window and called a greeting in Luganda. He ignored it. Benedict gingerly got out of the Land Rover and approached the man. I saw the man's knuckles tighten round the knife's handle and I prayed Benedict wouldn't come to any harm. Benedict greeted the 'guard' and I overheard the man reply, 'What's that?' Initially I thought he was pointing at the vehicle, but then I realised he was pointing at me; he had never seen a white woman before and was simply frightened. Minutes later, he had discarded his *panga* and Benedict helped him dismantle the roadblock. As we drove through, the man turned his back towards me and covered his face. I stopped the car and suggested that Benedict give him some bananas as a thank you. In the rear-view mirror, I watched the man smile as he received them, but I wondered if he would ever have the courage to eat them.

12.

Elephants Roam in the Moonlight

In between visits to Sigulu, I was still based at Buluba, teaching new leprosy assistants and visiting the county units and aid posts in my capacity as Leprosy Control Officer for Busoga.

As a thank you for their hard work, we introduced a yearly trip for the leprosy assistants. It could only be a short holiday, as it meant leaving a skeleton staff at each of the leprosy centres to carry on with the treatment. I allowed the assistants to choose their destination and they had opted to spend a few days at the Murchison Falls, hundreds of miles north of Buluba. The Falls are surrounded by the national park of the same name, covering an area of about 1,500 square miles. The Victoria Nile River flows through the park on its way to Lake Albert. It was a Mecca for tourists owing to its rich and varied wildlife; below the Falls lived some of the largest crocodiles in the world.

I drove Buluba's Land Rover while Sister Damiano drove one that we'd borrowed from the district. We couldn't afford to stay in the hotel at the Falls, but there was a dormitory with a kitchen for the use of schools. We had been informed that there was a teacher's room attached to the dormitory that Sister Damiano and I could sleep in. When we arrived, the head game ranger showed us our accommodation, and we were alarmed to discover that the teacher's room was divided from the rest of the dormitory by only half a mud wall.

All the leprosy assistants were young men so the sleeping situation wasn't suitable. Sister and I discussed the problem: we didn't feel we could stay at the park's Paraa Lodge Hotel while the boys slept in the dormitory. I remembered that the tent I used on Sigulu was in the back of the Buluba Land Rover.

'Would it be possible to pitch our tent outside?' I asked the game ranger.

'That's fine,' he said, 'so long as you're aware there'll be moonlight tonight.' He looked up at the sky and sighed. Before I could ask him what he meant, he continued: 'And you know the elephants roam in the moonlight.' He gave a little nod of his head and walked away. I turned to Sister, who suggested that we pitch the tent between the Land Rovers. Before I had time to reply, Ludovico emerged from the dormitory.

'*Nnyabo*, I need somewhere else to sleep.'

'Why?' I asked him.

'I'm not a leprosy assistant.'

'I know that.' Then it dawned on me. 'Oh, so the other leprosy assistants won't let you sleep in the dormitory with them. Never mind, Ludovico, you can sleep in one of the Land Rovers and guard us from the elephants in the moonlight!' I laughed, although part of me suspected the game ranger might have been serious. Ludovico seemed pleased at this suggestion and went to collect his belongings from the dormitory. After the long drive I was keen to go to bed. I had become used to sleeping in a tent and savoured drifting out of consciousness to the sound of the waterfall carried by the night breeze.

'*Nnyabo, Nnyabo*!'

'Yes, Ludovico, what is it?' I yawned.

'A great big *helephant* just about to put his feet on the tent.'

My eyes shot open. A giant shadow blocked the moonlight from flooding through the canvas. Fortunately, neither Sister nor I panicked: we lay completely still, holding our breath, as we watched the shadow looming closer. Suddenly there was a crash: Ludovico had opened the Land Rover door, and then slammed it – hard. From the shadow a trunk flew into the air and, as suddenly as it had materialised, the elephant's silhouette disappeared back into the bush. Silence.

Over the sound of my heart beating, I heard a noise. I felt my body tense. At first I suspected another animal, but then I recognised the sound. It was a human laugh; several people laughing. Cautiously, I poked my head out of the tent. The leprosy assistants had watched the whole episode through the dormitory window, and were unable to control their hilarity. I shook my head. They may have found it funny, but Sister Damiano and I didn't sleep for the rest of the night, despite Ludovico bringing us a cup of tea. I was relieved he had had the sense to act while Sister and I lay frozen on our camp beds.

The following day, once bright sunshine had replaced the cool moonlight, I saw the more amusing side. I was having some time to myself sitting on the veranda of the beautiful Paraa Lodge Hotel set within the game park. Sister Damiano and I had kindly been offered the use of the hotel facilities by the manager. It was teatime and I sat in the half-shade, sipping a cup of Ugandan-grown tea and basking in my surroundings as the sun lost its earlier intensity. Ludovico and the leprosy assistants had gone to explore. Sister Damiano joined me, admitting that she felt very tired; not only had our sleep been disturbed, but she had started taking mepacrine instead of quinine for malaria and it had turned her skin, and even the whites of her eyes, sickly yellow. It wasn't dangerous; it just looked as though she was suffering from jaundice. We were happy to sit quietly, watching the game park. The view was stunning. A baby elephant and its mother stood a short distance away. They seemed small compared to the silhouette that had kept me awake most of the night. As we watched, the hotel cat approached the huge animals. The young elephant looked up from his grazing. As the cat sauntered nearer, the elephant edged round the side of a bush. The cat changed course. Playfully, the little elephant galloped round the other side of the bush. I realised I was watching a cross-species game of 'tag'! The mother elephant simply watched, as we did and, once the game was over, she and her baby trundled off into the dense bush.

During the regime of Idi Amin in the 1970s, the Murchison Falls were renamed the Kaberega Falls after Kaberega, who was a powerful and infamous rebel. The hotel and parts of the park were destroyed by Amin's soldiers, along with much of the wildlife. The name reverted back to the Murchison Falls following the downfall of Idi Amin although both names are still used. The park has now been restored to at least some of its former beauty and continues to be a popular tourist attraction. It even has a new Paraa Lodge Hotel.

Some time after the trip, I was travelling to a county unit with one of the young leprosy assistants who had been on the Murchison Falls trip. His name was Ponsiano. The Ugandans were renowned for giving the Europeans nicknames; they wouldn't tell us what our nickname was so they could have a conversation about us in our presence and we wouldn't know they were taking about us. Ponsiano was chatting away as I drove the Land Rover along one of Busoga's better roads. He was recounting something that had happened earlier that week.

'Who said that, Ponsiano?' I asked.

He didn't answer.

'Ponsiano, who said it?'

Nothing. I couldn't understand why he wouldn't tell me.

'Come on, Ponsiano, who was it?'

'"Sister be quick" said it,' he mumbled.

'Who's "Sister be quick"?'

No answer.

'Who is "Sister be quick", Ponsiano?' In the silence it began to dawn on me. 'Is "Sister be quick" me?'

'Yes, *Nnyabo*.'

'And why do you call me "Sister be quick"?'

He hesitated, then shrugged. 'Well, *Nnyabo*, every time you tell us to do something, you follow it with "and be quick about it!".'

I hadn't even realised. After this incident I caught myself saying these words a few times, and just about managed to stop myself.

I tried always to treat the leprosy assistants well. I spent more time with Benedict than any of the others. His fun and humour was tempered with his sensible nature; he wouldn't let me do anything if he thought it might harm me. It was unusual for me to be irritable, but one morning I had been unduly cross with one of the students. A little later, I was in my office and overheard Benedict and another student outside the door.

'Don't go in there,' Benedict warned him. 'Sister's got a fever this morning.'

During my general nursing training I had been a keen sportswoman and often found time to swim and play tennis. I was even a member of the team that competed in the regional inter-hospital tennis competition. At Buluba, we had a badminton net, some racquets and shuttlecocks, brought back by one of the Sisters when she had been home on leave. We also discovered we could buy replacement shuttlecocks in Kampala. So we marked out a court in the compound's red dust and I taught some of the patients to play. Not only was it enjoyable, it was good, for those that could, to exercise their limbs. On one occasion, I was playing with three of the patients when a thunderstorm suddenly broke. Almost instantly the court was streaming with troughs of red water as the torrential rain mingled with the dust. We abandoned our racquets and rushed inside with the rest of Buluba's residents. Thunderstorms during the short rainy period could be extremely dangerous. The rain can be so heavy that roads become impassable within minutes. People caught out in such downpours can be drowned.

From the safety of the staff quarters, I saw lightning fork down, followed almost immediately by a growl of thunder. While we sheltered from the storm, a lady who lived in one of the houses at Buluba remembered she had left clothes drying on some of the bushes. As she ran outside to collect them with her twelve-month old baby tied to her back, the lightning bolt I had seen from the window struck her dead. We were notified that something had happened by the wailing of a neighbour, which we only heard as the thunder began to subside.

When I reached the scene, I saw the woman lying face down in the red mud. I assumed the baby had been killed, but as I bent down I realised she was asleep, soaking wet, on her dead mother's back. I untied the material that had been used to strap the baby to her mother and handed her to a patient who had come to help. We could do nothing for the mother, but the baby suffered no ill effects. A few days later, her father took her to his relations who lived in a nearby village. We were able to find a lady in America who sponsored the child's education. The child grew into a delightful and happy young woman, despite the early tragedy in her life.

For several years, a Dutchman called Mr Goes worked for the mission. He was a hunter, but he looked after the cars and tractors at Buluba. He would entertain the staff and the children with his tales of hunting the elephant and buffalo deep in the African bush. He didn't hunt for sport but only shot animals that had been mortally wounded and left for dead by poachers.

For a time, Dr Blenska and I both had dogs: Sophie was mine, of course. Dr Blenska had a white Jack Russell terrier whose name now escapes me (except that it was Polish) – I'll call it Patch for now. While we worked, the dogs would run around the compound, digging holes in the badminton court and often providing a source of amusement to the children when they weren't in school. One morning while Dr Blenska was busy at the hospital, I observed a group of children running and squealing after Mr Goes.

'Help! A big snake's got Doctor's dog. Come quick.'

Mr Goes slung his rifle over his shoulder and marched after the children. I hurried after them to the other side of the compound where a huge python lay basking in the sunshine. Lazily it watched us, its black tongue teasing the air. A Jack Russell-sized lump distorted its markings a quarter of the way along its length.

Mr Goes took aim and shot the python in the head. Immediately he knelt beside the dead, but slowly writhing, snake, unsheathed his hunting knife and sliced through the scales overlying the lump. With a second deft incision, he opened the snake's gullet and stomach and pulled Patch out, limp but still alive. He carried the dog over to the water pump, quickly showered off the reptilian saliva, and rubbed Patch's flanks to stimulate him. Patch sat up, decided he'd had enough of the shower treatment and ran off to say hello to the children. Without the quick response of Mr Goes the hunter, Patch would have been dead, suffocated by the python's saliva and the squeezing of its stomach muscles.

Kinawampere was the largest of the county units, about forty-five miles north-east from Buluba. There was already a large treatment centre in the compound and there were plans for expansion, with a house for the leprosy assistant, and accommodation for visitors – such as me – who might need to stay overnight. Contributions to our work at Kinawampere came from some unexpected sources. While I was on leave in England, I visited St Thomas à Becket, a comprehensive school in Moreton, on the Wirral. Encouraged by the headmaster, I taught some of the children about the leprosy work I was involved with in Uganda. The school made it their project to raise funds to buy 100 chicks for Kinawampere Leprosy Centre.

I'd only been back in Uganda a few days when I had a notice from Entebbe airport to collect the chicks. I found them as soon as I arrived, directed to the crate by the loud chirping. Initially I took the tiny birds back to Buluba where the Sister in charge of the farm cared for them until they were big enough to be taken to Kinawampere. At Kinawampere, they were shared out between the inpatients and fifteen of the more local outpatients, so the centre's resident leprosy assistant could keep a check on the progress of the hens. Tribal custom prevented the women and girls from eating eggs, but they were allowed to eat the meat from old hens that had stopped laying, or surplus cockerels, and this provided their diets with much needed protein.

Some time later, we were visited by a German friend, with his English wife, who had a large farm at Kipkabus, near Eldoret in Kenya. There was an open invitation for Sisters from the mission to stay on this beautiful farm as a retreat from the leprosy work. I had the pleasure of visiting them on many occasions. During their visit to the mission, they offered us three of their Jersey heifers for Kinawampere, which we gladly accepted. The patients responded to the news by building a shed for their new livestock. The local veterinary officer helped them build a spray race so the cattle could be individually sprayed against trypanosomiasis as often as was necessary. When everything was ready, I applied for permission from the Ugandan government to import the cattle, while our friends on the farm obtained an export licence to take them out of Kenya. The District Medical Officer lent me one of the department's lorries to transport the animals.

It was a long journey to Kenya and back. Although a driver had been provided, I wanted to accompany him to the farm – and the cattle on the return journey. As we drove back down the road to Kinawampere with our bovine cargo, I could hear drums playing. People were dancing amidst the home-made flags that had been draped around the compound. We opened the back of the lorry and allowed the heifers to wander down the ramp and into their new home. They flicked their tails and glanced about nervously, until one of the patients appeared carrying a bag of their food. Once they had something to eat, they seemed perfectly at home. There was no problem about a water supply for them as Kinawampere had large rainwater tanks.

The three young heifers grew well and as each of them came into season, we took them to visit the bull at Buluba, hoping that when we brought them back to Kinawampere they would be pregnant. In time, each of these heifers calved and produced plenty of creamy Jersey milk. We found the milk was a much more hygienic way for the out-patients to swallow their leprosy treatment tablets. Previously they had brought bottles containing water of a strange colour and questionable cleanliness. As the milk yield improved, there was sufficient to make tea for the adults and provide a daily mug for all the children. They clearly enjoyed its flavour and I was delighted that they were benefiting nutritionally. In time, Kinawampere was able to buy a small van that one of the patients would use to deliver milk to the other leprosy centres.

On one occasion, I was at Kinawampere when one of the heifers calved but retained the placenta. We sent one of the young patients to fetch the local veterinary officer, but he came back on his own with a message that the vet had gone to another case. There was a danger that the placenta would become necrotic within the heifer's womb, putting the heifer's life, or at least her future fertility, at risk. I decided to try and help her.

Since I'm rather small in stature, the first problem was being able to reach into the animal: I had to stand on a box to get my arm far enough into the cow to grasp the placenta. I hadn't realised how much more difficult it would be than dealing with a human. Eventually, though, I managed to get the complete placenta out. The heifer seemed to suffer no ill effects and produced a second calf the following year.

Such projects helped not only the leprosy patients but also their relatives. It would have been good to do a similar thing for the other smaller leprosy centres but, sadly, time and funds were against us.

13.

Along the Smugglers' Roads

The lights were on in Buluba's guest house as I pulled up after a day at a treatment centre. I didn't think anything of it, as we often had visitors. I quickly unloaded the Land Rover and went inside. On the way, I met several of the staff.

'Sister Alcantara wants you to go to the guest house,' I was told.

'Is it urgent?' I asked. 'I mean, do I have time for a cup of tea first?'

'Sister Alcantara said to tell you to go to her as soon as you returned.'

'What's it about? Who's in the guest house?'

'We don't know.'

I looked at their faces. They were clearly as mystified as I was.

There was an armed soldier standing guard outside the guest house. I approached him anxiously, wondering what on earth I had done. As I reached him, he saluted me and opened the door. Inside the room Sister Alcantara, the *Kyabazinga* of Busoga and his aide-de-camp hushed their conversation. The *Kyabazinga*, or tribal king, was also the current vice-president of Uganda. Satisfied that I was alone, Sister Alcantara invited me to join them at the table. I greeted the *Kyabazinga* and accepted the cup of tea Sister offered me. For a few moments no one said anything. I waited, sipping the welcome beverage, for Sister to explain what was going on.

'The *Kyabazinga* has come to us for help,' she began. 'Nothing we say tonight must leave this room, understand?'

I nodded. She drew a breath and then looked at the king. He looked towards the door and the windows and, seeming satisfied, leaned towards me.

'I think the president is plotting to have me assassinated. I need to get out of Uganda and into Kenya quickly.' He glanced at Sister Alcantara. 'And quietly,' he added.

I can't imagine what sort of expression crossed my face, but Sister Alcantara continued, 'Sister, you know most of the minor roads better than anyone else at Buluba. I am asking you to help. But I am *not* ordering you.'

'There is hardly any petrol left in the Land Rover,' I answered mechanically, 'certainly not enough to get to Kenya and back.'

'I will arrange to have the petrol tank filled at army headquarters,' said the *Kyabazinga*.

Sister Alcantara allowed me a moment to let it all sink in, before she went on: 'If we do this, Sister, we should travel in two cars. You would drive the *Kyabazinga* and his aide-de-camp and I would drive the second car carrying the queen and her maid.'

I felt much happier about the prospect knowing that Sister Alcantara intended to come as well, although a thought had occurred to me.

'What about when we reach the Kenyan border post?'

'Normally only white people have to produce their passports so it shouldn't be a problem.'

Sister Alcantara explained that we would drive into Kenya as far as Eldoret. There, the aide-de-camp, dressed in plain clothes, would take over driving the second vehicle, which was his own private car, and would convey all the royal party to their final destination. Meanwhile, Sister Alcantara and I would continue in the Land Rover to Kipkabus, the farm owned by our friends Herman and Edith Klapprott. Their farm was only about thirty miles from Eldoret. If we stayed there for a few days, it would arouse no suspicion. It would be assumed we were taking a short holiday.

'But you don't have to do this, Sister,' Sister Alcantara reminded me. 'It's your choice.'

At about three o'clock the following morning, we left Buluba. As discussed, the *Kyabazinga* and his aide-de-camp were in the Land Rover with me, and Sister Alcantara followed in the aide-de-camp's car with the queen and her maid. I led our small convoy along the smugglers' roads. I knew them well as they were all short cuts to the various leprosy centres and roadside clinics. The night sky lit our stealthy progress. There were no other cars. At one point, a small deer appeared suddenly in the Land Rover's headlamps. For a second it froze, but as I touched the brakes, it ran away into the forest to our left.

None of us had spoken since the prayers we had said together before we set out. In the quiet, I tried to enjoy the beautiful stars and rich-smelling foliage. I didn't want to dwell on what might happen if we were caught – on what might happen to the *Kyabazinga*; to Sister; to me. I scolded myself for my wandering imagination: I'd decided to do it, so there was no point worrying now.

It took three hours to reach the border because we used the back roads. Despite my attempts to rein in my imagination, I began to wonder afresh what would happen at the checkpoint. We were relying purely on the assumption that the soldiers would be checking only the passports of non-Africans entering Kenya. The *Kyabazinga* was a well-known public figure. If any of the border guards looked closely at the occupants of our vehicle, he would be recognised.

About half a mile from the border, the *Kyabazinga* slumped in his seat and pulled his trilby down low over his face, feigning sleep.

I tried to stop my hand from trembling as I handed over my passport for the soldier to stamp.

'Where are you going, *Nnyabo*?' the guard asked as he scanned the document.

'Eldoret,' I smiled.

'And how long are you going for?'

'Just a few days. No more than a week.' I tried to sound light-hearted; like somebody looking forward to her holiday.

He handed back my passport and I got back into the car.

'Enjoy your stay!' he called.

I started the engine and drove as fast as I dared over the border. A few miles inside Kenya, Sister Alcantara gestured for me to stop. She pulled up behind me and got out.

'Have a drink, Sister.' She handed me a bottle of Pepsi through the open Land Rover window. Her eyes were bright with the adventure. Drinking it, I realised how dry my lips and mouth had become.

A few hours later, we arrived in Eldoret where we were due to part company. The *Kyabazinga* thanked us as he climbed into the car with his wife and their staff. Sister Alcantara and I continued to Kipkabus in Buluba's Land Rover.

We received a tremendous welcome from our friends at their farm. It was right up in the highlands, 6,000 feet above sea level, encircled by great pine and wattle trees. We enjoyed four relaxing days with Mr and Mrs Klapprott, as part of our charade, before Sister Alcantara deemed it time to return to Uganda.

Due to the sensitivity of the situation, it was very important that no one knew what we had done. Only one sister at the convent knew; Sister Felicity, the 87-year-old aunt of Ruth, who had accompanied me to Sigulu, had been told of the plan. She would've died rather than divulge anything.

The journey back to Uganda was a far less stressful affair. A few days after arriving at Buluba we read in the local paper that the *Kyabazinga* had been spotted in Nairobi with two European ladies. I can assure you it was not us!

Between these escapades, I continued to be dedicated to the treatment of leprosy across Busoga. Dr Blenska recognised that if leprosy treatment was to continue and improve across the whole of Uganda, it would have to be integrated into the general medical service of the country. There had been a recommendation from the World Health Organisation to teach leprosy to all grades of medical and paramedical personnel. Dr Blenska and I took this recommendation very seriously.

Despite all we'd achieved, there was still a great stigma and fear attached to leprosy, even among people working in the medical field. The fallacy that it couldn't be cured was still widely accepted. Dr Blenska worked extremely hard with African doctors and medical students to try to change this attitude.

In June 1969, final-year medical students from Makerere University Medical School spent some time at Buluba under Dr Blenska's direction. This enabled them to become acquainted with leprosy diagnosis and control.

Whole classes from Makerere Medical School and Jinja Nurses' Training School began to spend study days at Buluba. We even took them with us to the county units and aid posts, continually trying to teach them that leprosy was not something to be feared. Even so, many of the students were absolutely petrified.

One year I was on leave, staying with my parents on the Wirral. The week before Christmas, I had to attend a leprosy conference at Amsterdam University, in the company of Dr Leiker, a consultant leprologist from Holland and Mr Kober, the Secretary General of the German Leprosy Relief Association (DAHW). This organisation had been very generous in financing much of the work in Uganda, including a budget specifically for my work. Before I left home for Amsterdam, I asked my mother if there was anything she would like me to buy for her.

'Bring some cigarettes and cigars,' she said.

So, at the airport, I bought cigarettes and cigars. As I was counting out my money, the lady at the counter spoke to me.

'I'm afraid, Sister, you've got too many to get through Customs. But if you want to give it a go, they may not say anything.'

'I'll give it a go, then,' I said.

Thick snow delayed the flight to London, from where I was to get a connecting flight to Liverpool. The steward came to see me during the flight and told me not to wait for my luggage but to hurry through the airport, as they were holding the Liverpool plane for me. When we finally landed in London, I shot off the plane and was faced with the choice of the two Customs and Excise channels: red for imports to declare, or green for nothing to declare. The red channel had no queue so, in my haste to catch my connecting flight, I decided to go that way. The Customs officer smiled quizzically.

'What have you got to declare today, Sister?'

'Fifty cigars and 300 cigarettes,' I told him quite honestly.

He looked taken aback, and then he chuckled.

'Oh, be off with you!' he said, waving me through.

After a lovely Christmas with my parents, my leave was over and I returned to Uganda via Würzburg in Germany. Here I met with the DAHW committee to discuss the future plans for leprosy control in Busoga district. Now that it was possible to fly from Germany to Uganda, I could be back in Busoga the same day that I left Germany – back to the life and work that meant so much to me.

Some months later, I was driving down a narrow red dusty road on my way to one of the county units. My journey took me right past Nsumba, a small village of a dozen or so round mud dwellings with grass roofs.

The village was protected from the sun's heat by the waving fronds of the banana trees, and perfumed by the pink and white frangipani flowers. As I rounded the last bend before the settlement, I was expecting to hear happy chanting or the rhythmic tapping of wooden mallets on tree trunks as the villagers beat the bark of the mutuba tree to make barkcloth. The colour of the barkcloth – anything from pink to deepest red – was determined by the length of time the bark was beaten. This beautiful cloth was then used to make clothes, bedcovers, as part of a bride's dowry, or, at the end of life, to wrap the dead.

Gradually, over the sound of the Land Rover's engine, I could hear chanting – not the happy chanting I was expecting, but the death dirge. I wondered what could have happened and decided to stop.

Many of the villagers were too busy wailing to notice my arrival. A melancholy figure crouched on the ground. I bent down to greet her and then asked who had died and if I could do anything to help.

'Oh, *Nnyabo!*' she sighed, looking up at me with heavy eyes. 'It's too late for you to help now.'

And with this, she began her tale of woe. The village of Nsumba was famous for its Leghorn cockerel. This beautiful bird, with its brilliant red comb and a magnificent cape of green, blue and orange neck feathers, was affectionately known as Robin. Visitors to the village were afraid to go near him once they'd come under his fierce glare. He was often seen strutting around the huts, followed by his faithful harem of hens. The woman rose at this point in the story to demonstrate Robin's movement, jerking her arms and neck as she strutted like the cockerel. Despite the sombre mood, there was something about her gestures that made me want to laugh. She turned to me suddenly, her eyes wide and unblinking.

'And now,' she announced, 'he is dead!'

By this time a group of villagers had gathered round us, nodding in agreement as the story unfolded. When I asked her what had happened, she explained that he'd been struck with a mysterious malady. He had been seen staggering around, his eyes glazed, squawking incessantly. At this point the other villagers interjected with their own comments. Various remedies had been applied, I was told, including the witchdoctor's brew of banana juice and sand.

'An evil spirit had come into him,' someone next to me said. This was followed by nods and grunts from the little crowd. They had decided that the only thing to do was to put the poor bird out of his misery.

The news of Robin's death was relayed by bush telegraph and, while I was there, many came from the nearby villages to offer condolences. As the people continued to discuss the cause of Robin's demise they arrived at the diagnosis: the only one ever made in a case of unusual sickness – poisoning. As the rumours spread and the people whispered, the night watchman was named the chief suspect. There was circumstantial evidence – Robin had been seen in the vicinity of the watchman's hut just before his dreadful seizure.

Several villagers investigated and discovered traces of grain scattered on the ground around the night watchman's hut. One small pile of grain was wet, with an unmistakable smell – that of potent home-brewed beer.

'Yes,' the night watchman confessed morosely. 'I did spill a pot of beer there.'

The case was solved. Poor Robin had been drunk, not poisoned. He had probably returned to the pile of fermenting grain again and again, with very sad results.

After giving my condolences, I suggested than rather than waste the bird, they could eat him, as the meat would still be fresh.

'Oh no, *Nnyabo!*' they cried. 'What if the evil spirit enters us?'

I realised there would be no persuading them, so I left for the county unit, promising to try to find them another cockerel for the village. I smiled as I drove, knowing the patients I was about to see would probably demonstrate a ghoulish fascination with the news of Robin and his untimely end.

Some months after I had made my promise to the people of Nsumba, as I walked through the compound of one of the leprosy centres on a routine visit, I noticed that there were several cockerels strutting about, each competing to impress the hens. Large numbers of male birds weren't necessary for egg production; in fact, competition for limited female attention could result in serious fighting between the rival birds. I found the patient who was in charge of the poultry and asked him if I could buy one of the cockerels. We agreed a figure that would have been sufficient for two replacement hens, and I was allowed to choose the cockerel myself. None of them had the imposing presence or beauty of Robin, but one did stand out as being particularly handsome.

I shut the somewhat indignant bird in the back of my car and decided to make a detour to Nsumba on my way back to Buluba. I wondered how he would react to meeting his own harem at the village that was to be his new home.

As I drew near to Nsumba, wonderful aromas filled the vehicle, emanating from the coffee bushes that grew amongst the banana trees in the village *shamba* (the African version of an allotment, growing food crops such as bananas, sweet potatoes, maize and coffee). At that time of year, after the April (long) rains, the bushes were in full flower and the perfume was all-pervading.

The village people were not expecting me; I arrived to a charming scene. Some of the men were making bark-cloth, beating their mallets in rhythm to their chanting. Others were mixing clay to make their drinking pots. Several of the ladies were peeling matoke in preparation for the evening meal, while others were simply sitting and chatting. Children played games, kicking up clouds of dust, benignly overseen by the older men who were sitting on small stools, smoking their pipes. It was a privilege to witness such a natural spectacle, one that must have changed very little for hundreds of years.

As soon as I stopped the car and the villagers perceived they had a visitor, the picture of tranquillity evaporated, and I climbed out to cries of greeting. I reached into the back of the vehicle to gather up the newest member of the village community, ignoring the disgruntled feather-flapping. Once the villagers realised what I had brought with me, all of them, even the men making barkcloth, left what they were doing and crowded round. Almost immediately the singing and dancing began.

I handed the cockerel over to the village headman, who started to dance with it and then carried it around so that every person in Nsumba could touch it. Finally he tied it to a post to make sure it didn't escape. One of the women came from her hut with a bowl of water and some grain for the bird. I left the villagers celebrating, confident their replacement Robin would settle down happily in his new family.

14.

Hard Times

'*Nnyabo*! *Nnyabo*! Have you heard?'

'Heard what, child?' I bent down to the little boy who had run up to me and pawed the edge of my coat with his bandaged hand.

'We're at war, *Nnyabo*,' he grinned.

'War? Who's at war?'

He looked puzzled, and then shook his head.

'I'm not making it up, *Nnyabo*. I heard some of the grown-ups talking about it. It was on the radio.'

It was 25 January 1971. I had just finished packing the Land Rover in preparation for my usual Monday afternoon visit to a leprosy centre fifty miles away when the little boy ran to me. I straightened up and walked into Buluba's ward. The buzz hit me immediately. As I joined the conversations, I learned that a military coup had begun at Entebbe airport – at least, according to a radio transmission heard by one of the older leprosy patients. Exhilaration flowed through the voices of all who spoke. Every one of the patients seemed to have an opinion. Many Ugandans were fed up with Obote's government and saw the opportunity for a change of government as a good thing. Others were fearful; it was no good overthrowing one dictator for him to be immediately replaced with another. As missionaries and guests in the country, we steered clear of politics unless it was necessary to help someone in need, such as the *Kyabazinga*.

There was a radio in the office. I tuned it in to the appropriate station for any further news bulletins, but all that was playing was martial music. I discussed the situation with Sister Alcantara and we agreed to abandon my planned trip away from Buluba, at least until we had a clearer picture of what was happening. Not long after we'd made the decision, Ludovico appeared with a note for Sister Alcantara.

'It's from the bishop,' she said, peering at the piece of paper. 'He says he doesn't want us to leave the compound until the situation has been assessed.'

We tried to continue as normal. There was plenty I could do at Buluba, most of which was within earshot of a radio. Later in the afternoon, there was a broadcast stating why the army had taken over. This was followed by a further announcement that the army had asked General Idi Amin to take over leadership of Uganda.

Things appeared to settle down very quickly, and I continued to visit other leprosy centres in the district as I had done previously. Gradually, though, rumours of terrible atrocities and murders began to filter through to us from Buganda, our neighbouring county, but there was nothing to substantiate them, at least initially.

Near Buluba compound lived a prominent lawyer and his family. His wife would sometimes bring us clothing that her children had outgrown, for the patients. One day, a few months after the coup, she appeared in our compound to tell us what had happened to her family. Earlier that day, Amin's soldiers had paid her a visit. They had thrust her husband's bloodstained shirt at her, saying, 'Here is your husband.' Those of us who sat and prayed with her were deeply impressed by her quiet dignity and unwavering faith.

Despite the horror of what had happened, she firmly believed that her husband had gone to be with the Lord. What distressed her most was wondering what her husband had suffered before his death.

A week later, a young Ugandan priest visited us. He had lost a lot of weight since we had last seen him. We were having our tea when he arrived, so he joined us at the table. As he sat down with us, he said, 'Sisters, I have come to tell you, today I have received my passport to heaven.'

Calmly, he explained that he, together with several newspaper reporters, had been called to a meeting with General Amin in his offices in Kampala. During the meeting, Amin had told them they must always write the truth.

'What is the truth, your Excellency?' the young priest had asked.

Amin, enraged by the question, had stormed out of the meeting.

A few weeks after our conversation, the priest's charred remains were discovered in his burnt-out car in the Mabira forest. None of us could think of any reason why he would have been visiting this area. Before he had left us at Buluba, we had knelt for him to bless us. I remember feeling a great peace envelop me and I shall never forget this fine, brave young man.

When I was visiting leprosy patients and centres outside Buluba, the soldiers were my biggest problem. They seemed to have free rein to do whatever they wanted. They were very well-armed, nearly always drunk – and unpredictable.

I was travelling towards Kampala from Jinja when I had to stop at a roadblock. I wound down the Land Rover's window and greeted the soldier who approached. He thrust his head through the open window. I tried not to breathe, but I couldn't shut out the hot, stale beer-breath. Suddenly he grinned and turned to his armed companions.

'Let this one go. She speaks our language.'

I drove away, thanking God that I had escaped the soldiers unscathed. Once I was out of sight, I tried to wind the window up. Although I was desperate to get the stench of stale beer and tobacco out of my nostrils, I wanted to be safely encased within the vehicle. It was on my fourth attempt at winding up the window that I realised that my hand was shaking.

Every so often General Amin would visit the leprosy centre at Nyenga. One of the Sisters there used to make a special cake for him. She always had to keep a fresh one available, as she never knew when he was going to turn up with his entourage. He and his aide-de-camp would have a cup of tea and a piece of the cake.

Whenever Amin asked if anything was needed, most of the Sisters would make some non-committal reply, such as, 'I don't know, your Excellency.' However, occasionally someone would be bolder.

One day, when he put this question, one of the newer Sisters said, 'Well, your Excellency, we are struggling to collect the matoke for the patients. Our car is small. It wouldn't matter if the plantation was nearer, but because it's so far we can't get enough in one trip. So it's a problem.'

Amin turned to his aide-de-camp and said, 'Get a lorry for Sister!'

Months went by, though, and we continued to collect the matoke by car. I assumed it had been an empty promise.

Several weeks later, Benedict and I were driving to a leprosy centre when I saw General Amin and his entourage approaching from the other direction. I pulled into the side of the very narrow road to let them pass. Out of courtesy (Amin was the president of the country, after all), Benedict and I got out of the car, shutting the door so Sophie couldn't escape. When the presidential cars reached us, Amin wound down his window, so we walked over to greet him. He beamed at us.

'Good morning, Sister. And how is Soapy today?'

'Very well, your Excellency, thank you.'

'Good, good. And are you off to a leprosy centre, now?'

'Yes, your Excellency.'

'How are the other Sisters?'

'They are all well, your Excellency.'

'That is good. And do you need anything at the mission centre?'

'I don't know, your Excellency.'

'Ah well. Have a good journey, Sister.' His smile widened, then he wound up the window and the conversation was over. As his car drove away, I couldn't help wondering what dubious scheme he was planning next.

Another time, it was the day before a feast day. One of Buluba's cows had been slaughtered and it was my job to take some of the meat to the leprosy centre at Nyenga. The journey was about twenty-six miles. I'd offered to take one of the resident patients with me for an outing: it was often beneficial for the patients to be taken outside Buluba, and the young man I asked was delighted to come. Our journey took us across the bridge that spanned the river at the Owen Falls dam, just outside Jinja.

As we approached the bridge, we could see a group of soldiers on the Buganda side.

'Shall we go back?' my companion asked, chewing his bottom lip.

'It's too late. They've seen us now.'

'We could still go back.'

'They've got guns,' I replied, edging the Land Rover across the bridge, and bringing it to a stop a few yards from the soldiers. I wound the window down and sat waiting. Two of them strode over. I greeted them, but they ignored it. The patient fixed his eyes on his feet. I held tightly to the steering wheel waiting for them to speak.

'Where are you going?'

'We're going to Nyenga,' I replied.

'What have you got in the car?'

'Meat.'

'What kind of meat?'

'Meat from a cow.'

'Where are you going with it?'

'I'm going to Nyenga,' I repeated.

'We want the meat.'

'I'm sorry,' I said quietly. 'You can't have the meat.'

The patient next to me seemed to visibly shrink into his seat.

'We want the meat.'

'I'm sorry, but you can't have it.'

The soldier who had been speaking swung away from me. I heard a click and knew that one of the guns had been primed. My interrogator moved out of the way to show one of the other soldiers pointing his gun directly at the car. I gripped the steering wheel tighter and closed my eyes for a moment, asking for God's help in this situation, wondering if I'd soon be seeing him face to face. Suddenly an idea struck me. I opened my eyes.

'All right,' I said to the soldier's back. 'You can have the meat.'

My companion let out a breath. The soldier turned back towards me, frowning.

'But,' I continued, 'do you know where this meat came from?'

'No!' he snapped.

'Do you know Buluba?'

'No!'

'Well, Buluba is the hospital for the leprosy patients and the leprosy patients have killed a cow, and I'm taking its meat to Nyenga to the other leprosy patients because it's a big feast day tomorrow.'

He didn't reply immediately, but I'd watched the whites of his eyes betray his fear at the word 'leprosy'. He took a step back, raised his gun and banged it twice on the Land Rover's bonnet. 'Go!' he said and waved the car across.

Once I'd turned the first corner and we were safely out of sight, I stopped the car. I couldn't drive any further. I took some deep breaths. The lad next to me was dripping with perspiration.

'Oh, *Nnyabo*! We could have been killed.'

'Well, we weren't, were we?'

I reached over and took his hands in mine and we closed our eyes.

'Thank you, Lord, for your protection. Thank you for keeping us safe. And Lord, please don't let the soldiers be on the bridge on our return journey. Amen.'

'Amen,' he whispered.

And I put the car in gear and carried on to Nyenga.

When we returned to Buluba there was no one on the bridge at Owen Falls dam.

I was in the office going through some papers one night, while Sophie snoozed on my feet under the desk. Suddenly she growled. Seconds later, two young leprosy assistants burst in.

'*Nnyabo*! *Nnyabo*! There's a whole crowd of soldiers in the compound. Will you hide us?'

I shuffled the papers into a pile. 'What do they want?' I asked.

'We didn't stay to find out. Please, *Nnyabo*!'

The poor men looked terrified.

'You stay in the office and put the light out,' I told them. 'I'll go and see what the soldiers want.'

When I went out, I saw a huge lorry in the compound with the soldiers leaning languidly against it. One of them handed me the keys.

'A gift from his Excellency,' he saluted.

So Amin had been faithful in his promise to provide us with a lorry. Several months had elapsed since he'd told his aide-de-camp to 'Get a lorry for Sister' and we hadn't really expected that he would. We were grateful, of course, but I couldn't help wondering which poor soul had lost his lorry.

15.

Wereba (Goodbye)

One of the hardest decisions I have ever had to make was the one to leave Uganda and the people I had come to love. I'd known for some time that the day would come, but had never imagined that it would be so soon.

In the mid 1970s, I had returned home on leave and was visiting my parents on the Wirral. During all the years I was out in Uganda, my mother wrote to me every week, without fail. However, when I arrived home on this particular leave, I realised that she had been economical with the details and truth about the extent of her and my father's problems. I soon began to recognise how difficult life had become for them. By this time, they were both in their eighties, lonely and struggling to cope. My brother had never fully recovered from his war wounds and also had to care for an invalid wife, so he could only be of limited help to them.

I was faced with an agonising choice: to leave my beloved Uganda and the precious work I was doing there, or to stay in England and care for my parents. There was very little time in which to make a decision. Every day of my leave, I prayed and prayed. In the night hours, as I lay awake, I asked God to help me to make the right choice. Slowly I began to realise that the work I had been doing in Uganda was well established and would carry on with

Dr Blenska at the helm and with the support of Sister Alcantara, whether I was still there or not. At the same time I knew that it would not be long before the leprosy care was integrated into the Ugandan medical service – the ultimate goal of our work over the years.

And so I arrived at the answer my prayers had sought; I would not return to Uganda but would stay in England and care for my parents for as long as they had need of me. This I did. When I first came home, I was still under the rules of my Order and supported by my parents. After four to six months I received my dispensation from Rome to leave the Order, and obtained a nursing post at the local hospital.

Much had been achieved in the treatment of leprosy during my years at Buluba. Although Dr Blenska and I had been the driving force for a lot of the work, we couldn't have done anything like as much without the support that we had. The trained leprosy assistants, the local ministers of health, the schoolteachers, all played their part. The District Medical Officer not only gave me permission to visit Sigulu and the other islands, but also lent me a boat, a skipper and much of the medical equipment I used in the clinics. Without the all-important cooperation of the chiefs, we would have achieved very little. It was the working together of all these people that ensured the establishment of the Leprosy Control System across Busoga.

Today, leprosy treatment has been fully integrated into Uganda's general medical service. The centres at Buluba and Kumi have been turned into hospitals treating tuberculosis and other conditions as well as leprosy.

One person who deserves significant credit is Sister Alcantara. She was a woman before her time. She saw the future; she saw the way Uganda was going to go, and the need to change the way in which leprosy was approached. It was she who gave me my head with the pioneering work that I was doing. Everything I did, I talked over with her. Had it not been for Sister Alcantara, we would not have been able to link our training at Buluba to that at the Protestant leprosy centre at Kumi. This wisest of women had a brilliant sense of humour and a genuine love for the Africans she worked among. I feel blessed to have worked under her.

I had been in England for about four years when Dr Blenska left Buluba, having worked there for nearly thirty years. Through her writing and knowledge of leprosy she became well known in the field as an outstanding leprologist. Her records and specimens were second to none. Several countries honoured her with medals, financial awards and academic scholarships in her name, including the USA, the Vatican and her homeland, Poland. All this was taken in her stride, and in no way altered her great love for her leprosy patients. Her bright smile and kind words continued to convey the same warmth they had when she first arrived in Uganda. Although I missed her greatly when I left Buluba, I consider it a privilege to have known her. Over the years, since we left Uganda, we have met in England on several occasions and still keep in touch.

Some time after both my parents had died, I was clearing their garage and I came across an old leather suitcase I'd never seen before. It was locked and I thought perhaps it might contain money. I managed to force the catch and, as the lid flew open, letters spilled out onto the floor – every single letter I had written to my mother over the thirty or so years I was away. I read through them all, reliving some of the adventures and tragedies I had experienced in Africa. The find provided the stimulus and the help I needed to write this book.

I was inspired, as I had been from the beginning of my missionary life, by this lyrical piece:[1]

> O African night, your stillness is awe-inspiring! Not a breath of wind disturbs the leaves of the trees and bushes. Millions of shining stars in a blue-black sky look down on the immense stretches of land and water, swamps where papyrus grows, on the scrub and jungle. Stillness, but not silence, for throughout the hours of darkness, there is a cacophony of sound from the chirping of thousands of crickets and croaking of frogs. In the warm air one breathes in the heavy perfume from the waxen blooms of the frangipani. Fireflies, with their fairy lamps lighten the undergrowth. And down by the shores of the Lake, there are the grunts and snorts of the hippos. The shriek of the hyena and its weird laughter rends the air, with the occasional howling of a wandering dog reminding man that the night belongs to the animals. But, in spite of these sounds, a strange stillness prevails, is almost felt. Then, from afar, suddenly a drum sounds beating out its monotonous tune, accompanied by the plaintive notes of the dongo. Far into the night there is the tireless beating of the drum and the fingering of the dongo, with perfect rhythm and harmony, to a tune that never varies. But a few hours before sunrise, for a brief spell, the African world quietens. The crickets stop their chirping, the frogs their croaking, all is quiet and at rest. Stillness and silence reign supreme over the plains and hills of this wonderful land.

Although many years have passed since I left Uganda, my love for its wonderful people and its beauty are seared into my memory, never to be forgotten. It is truly the Pearl of Africa. At its centre is the rich cultural heritage of the various tribes: of music, dance and folklore, handed down through the generations. Unrestricted by the trappings of civilisation, an adventurous spirit and zest for life saturates everything the Ugandans do. And around them is their spectacular land. From the snow-capped Mountains of the Moon in the west, to the shimmering waters of Lake Victoria Nyanza in the south, the country glitters in the tropical light. From the hills of Ankole, where the long-horned cattle browse, to the low rolling hills of Buganda with its vivid banana groves and papyrus-filled swamps . . . each place with its own natural harmony. It is a wild and beautiful land: an Eden. This Eden, too, had its serpent – disease was rampant. Plague, smallpox, sleeping sickness, malaria and leprosy all served to tarnish the Pearl. These illnesses, like natural disasters, were believed to be caused by malignant spirits.

But, like all precious stones, the Pearl endures. Following its emergence as an independent nation in 1962, it endured the tribal wars and divisions that often afflict young nations. It endured, though barely, fear, torture, brutality and death at the hands of Idi Amin's forces: his trigger-happy soldiers almost annihilated much of the country's wildlife. All these things have dulled the Pearl for a time. But, in spite of this, no one can take away the beauty that God has laid at Africa's heart. As I write, the clouds of warfare seem to be disappearing and the blessing of peace is returning.

That the Pearl of Africa should be restored to its former beauty is surely the prayer of all who love this country and its precious people. There is an African saying 'He who drinks Nile water will always return'. I wish!

Endnotes

7. Leprosy Control – the Dream Becomes Reality

[1] In retrospect, 'wasting disease' was most likely AIDS, though it was not known as such at this time. A patient would be brought to us 'to die because he (or she) has wasting disease'.

10. Eggs, Fish and Banana Leaves

[1] An *askari* is a native African police officer or soldier, especially one serving a colonial administration.

11. The Bishop Visits Sigulu

[1] A *dongo* is a handmade musical instrument made by fixing very thin strips of metal to a piece of wood, each metal strip producing a different note. The instrument was played by the thumb striking the metal strips. The sound produced was quite beautiful; similar to a harp.

[2] A *panga* is a large, broad-bladed African knife used as a weapon or as an implement for cutting heavy jungle growth, sugar cane, etc.

15. *Wereba* (Goodbye)

[1] *O African Night* came from a sheet of paper slipped into an old book in a cupboard in the convent where I was doing my training. I modified it to use in my prayers. Original source unknown.